Other Hilarious Books
By Gil Gevins:

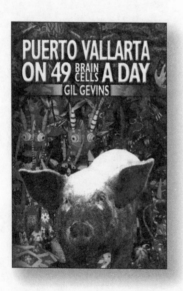

PUERTO VALLARTA
ON A DONKEY A DAY

PUERTO VALLARTA ON A DONKEY A DAY

Gil Gevins

COATIMUNDI PRESS
Oakland, California

No character in this book is based on that of a living
person. The reader will note that various references have
been made to places such as Puerto Vallarta, Oaxaca and
other localities in Mexico. I wish to make it absolutely clear
that no inhabitant past or present of those particular places
appears in these stories. Any similarity the reader might
observe between real persons and these fictitious characters
is purely coincidental.

Whether or not I myself exist is a metaphysical question
I will not take up at this time.

To Jack and Alan

Acknowledgement

I wish to take this opportunity to gratefully acknowledge the work of two people without whom this would have remained just a manuscript and never been successfully shaped and crafted into its current eye-pleasing form.

Mark Callanan (www.callananphoto.com), the brilliant Aussie photographer, is responsible for all of the photos. Mark is a man of great talent and generosity. Working with him was indeed a privilege.

The more arduous and prolonged task of taking my text and Mark's photos and making them into a book was performed expertly by Paul McBroome, the graphic wizard responsible for *Vallarta Lifestyles* Magazine as well as most of the *Viva Productions* publications. Paul combines talent, professionalism and expertise: all of the supremely desirable traits one would hope for in a graphic artist. The over-all appearance of this book is a result of his exceptional work, and I thank him most sincerely for doing such an outstanding job. (virtualvallarta.com)

And thanks to Joy Eckel.

Contents

We Know Trauma

The Cine Bahia was, in 1983, a charming old dinosaur of a theatre showing "first-run" American movies—six months to a decade after their initial release. My fiancée and I used to go there every Friday. The oft-played prints were badly scarred, frequently missing key scenes; and the muffled scratchy "sound system", a relic from World War II, rendered the dialogue all but incomprehensible. But we didn't mind. The air inside was cool enough to cuddle, and being force-fed Spanish subtitles was a wonderful way to improve my nascent foreign language skills.

Then Consuelo, my fiancée's mom, came to visit, and I became embroiled in a dramatic debacle of Old Testament proportions.

The Cine Bahia was going to put on an *"Obra de Arte"*, the first live drama to bless Vallarta's arid cultural shores in living memory. It was to be an historic occasion and the two women insisted that all three of us attend.

"Why do I have to go?" I whined. "I won't understand a word. I'll be bored spitless."

"We need an escort," Lucy replied. "And you make such a dashing *caballero*."

At that time, early on in our acquaintance, when Lucy asked me to do something, I was all but powerless to refuse. But sitting through what was bound to be a cheesy incomprehensible melodrama was more than I was prepared to endure.

"Can't you hire someone to go with you?" I pleaded.

"Like who?"

"I don't know. What's the gardener doing tonight?"

Once the three of us were seated in the third row of the cavernous dilapidated theatre, Lucy's sixty-eight-year-old mom turned to me and expressed her fervent hope that I would not be bored. She even offered to translate for me.

"No, please don't bother," I told her. "I'll just make up my own dialogue; it'll be more fun that way."

"God bless you," the saintly woman replied.

Slowly but surely the theatre proceeded to fill.

"So what's this award-winning drama about?" I yawned.

"I'm not sure," Lucy said. "Something to do with women in prison, I think."

"Sounds great," I mumbled. "Wake me up when it's over."

When the curtain finally parted we were indeed treated to the sight of three young women wearing drab grey shapeless smocks, and occupying an austere set representing the inside of a prison. The women were involved in an animated conversation, not one word of which I could understand.

"My mother's not going to like this," Lucy whispered urgently in my ear.

"Why, is it too racy for her?" I whispered back.

Lucy's mom was an old-fashioned, deeply religious woman, easily discomfited when it came to anything even slightly risqué.

"Oh my God!" Lucy gasped.

To my (shall we say) *pleasant* surprise, two of the actresses had slipped their formless dresses over their heads and were now revealed in the vast majority of their glory.

And glorious they were indeed: lithe, young, nubile and exceedingly pretty. In my excellent third-row stage-center seat, I was rendered all but witless by the criminal proximity of so much post-teen pulchritude. Like a badly bred St. Bernard, I began to pant.

Consuelo, meanwhile, was staring, not at the stage, but at the floor, taking slow deep breaths and repeatedly making the Sign of the Cross. Thus was she able to shield her eyes from the slings of outrageous visual stimuli. Unfortunately, there was not a great deal she could do to likewise protect her sensitive ears from the spicy dialogue, which apparently contained a good deal of "slang".

"What are they saying?" I whispered to Lucy.

"Never mind," she whispered back, shaking her head in disbelief as she cast anxious glances over at her hyperventilating mom.

Fortunately for me, it did not require an advanced degree in Spanish Literature to follow the plot. The still-clothed inmate (a newly interred "rookie") was being urged by her two naked cell mates to participate in certain activities one could only describe as "somewhat unorthodox". A scuffle ensued, a kind of mud-wrestling match without the mud, in the course of which the rookie was first subdued, then de-clothed and finally...

"Burp! Burp! Burp!"

Whenever Consuelo was upset or agitated, it went right to her upper digestive tract. Judging by the volume and frequency of her gastric eruptions, she was at the moment distraught indeed.

"Quiet!" several people sitting near us (all of them men) hissed indignantly.

"Burp! Burp! Burp!"

Lucy eyed her mother fearfully. "Come on," she said, preparing to get up, "let's go."

"Go?" I nearly shouted. "We just got here!"

Indeed, the play was only eight minutes old. And having witnessed its powerful opening, I was quite anxious to experience what was certain to be an extraordinary climax.

"Burp! Burp! Burp!"

Lucy eyed me evilly. Her mother was approaching extremis, while the men seated around us grew increasingly hostile.

To say that I was reluctant to leave my seat would be

the understatement of the millennium. It was as if some Unseen Hand had super-glued my buttocks to the sagging chair. Nonetheless, I somehow managed to stand up and accompany the two women to the lobby, all but dislocating my neck as I strained to look back over my shoulder.

By the time we reached the popcorn machine, Consuelo's burping had begun to subside. "That was terrible!" she declared in shocked tones, making the Sign of the Cross once again, just to be on the safe side.

"Disgraceful," I agreed. "Say, I have to use the men's room. Why don't you two ladies go on ahead. I'll catch up to you, uh, later."

"We'll wait for you," Consuelo said with her customary politeness.

"No, please don't inconvenience yourself..." I began.

"If you're not out of the 'bathroom' in five minutes," Lucy advised me, "you're sleeping on the floor tonight."

"Of course, honey. Hey, look who's here. It's Manuel."

"Who?"

"I'll be right back," I said, approaching a Mexican man I'd never seen before. "Where's the bathroom?" I asked him, stretching my Spanish to its very limits. "What time is it?" I prattled on. "I am happy. Are you also happy? How much does a beer cost?"

Then, before the confused fellow could run away, I rushed back to the ladies and said, "I just ran into an old friend I haven't seen in years. He invited me out for a beer. Why don't you two go ahead and..."

"Forget the floor," Lucy said through gritted teeth, "you're sleeping in the gutter. Where you belong."

"Ha, ha," I laughed. "What a sense of humor your daughter has! Lucy, can I speak to you in private, please?"

"Let's make a deal," I said, once I had gotten her alone. "What do you want? A new car? A boat? A trip to Europe? Name it, it's yours."

"All right," Lucy said, favoring me with a wry smile. "Go ahead and indulge your base instincts. As long as you let me know how it ends."

"I'll do better than that," I promised my future bride, "I'll *show* you how it ends. Hey, Manuel," I shouted across the lobby, "wait up, dude!"

What Did You Call Me?

Desperation can make a man do strange and unusual things. And I was desperate, indeed— desperate to be fired from my job at *Lucy's Cucu Cabaña*, one of the finest folk-art shops in all Mexico. Unfortunately, the owner of the shop (my wife) was a devilishly tolerant woman who refused to take my repeated store-related transgressions seriously. She'd had me chained there to the antique genuine wormwood desk for more than ten years, and I was beginning to feel as if I would ultimately expire there, assuring Canadian tourists with my last rattling breath that the bus to *Mismaloya* was in fact the one that said "*Mismaloya*" on it.

But then I received a phone call which almost changed my life.

The call was from Janice, an unrepentant gossip who also worked as a volunteer for our local theatre company. Janice got right to the point, after first filling me in (at length) on the latest local scandal. A prominent municipal functionary, it seemed, had been caught padding the payroll with phantom employees: his four grandchildren (ages two to six), a deceased aunt and the next-door neighbor's German Shepard (Otto Von Bismarck XIII), who was presumably filling a post in Foreign Relations. "But that's not the reason I'm calling," Janice informed me.

"You have a reason?"

She certainly did. A play about a middle-aged man

suffering from Alzheimer's was due to open in ten days, and suddenly they'd found themselves without an actor to fill the leading role. Could I think of *anyone* who might be suitable and/or interested?

"Janice, why are you asking *me*?"

Janice, who drank far too much coffee and often spoke like a nervous newscaster rattling off tabloid headlines, replied breathlessly, "Emergency! Calling everyone who speaks English! Auditions tomorrow!"

"I'm flattered," I said. "But what happened to Charlie Jenkins? I thought he had the part all wrapped up."

"Hit by a bus!" she gasped. "In critical condition! Driver fled! Being sought by police!"

"Calm down, Janice," I advised her. "I'll think about it. Call later. Don't hold breath."

After hanging up, I spent the next ten minutes sitting at my desk going insane with boredom. But then it suddenly dawned on me that I had just been handed a free pass (if I played my misfiring neurons correctly) to a front-row seat in the unemployment line. No, no, I thought, that's not right; you don't sit in a line, you stand in it. Where you sit is in an office, like I am sitting here in my antique chair, slowly dissolving in a pool of putrefying retail rot.

In order to prepare myself for the audition I decided upon the *Method* approach, whereby I would immerse myself so completely in the role that I *became* the character. By so doing, not only would I be following in the footsteps of my thespian heroes (Brando, DeNiro, PeeWee Herman), I would also be providing myself with a lame but plausible excuse for what I hoped my wife would consider actionable behavior.

The first customer of the morning was an old and valued client who lived in Vallarta for six months a year, and who was particularly fond of our sensational *Michoacan* masks. She had been in the shop the previous day ogling a particularly elaborate one for the better part of an hour.

"Good morning," she said cheerfully. "I've finally decided to get it."

"Good morning," I said. "Get what?"

"Why, the mask of course," she said, eyeing me uncertainly.

"Which mask?"

"The one I was looking at yesterday," she replied testily.

"You were here yesterday?"

"Yes, of course. Don't tell me you don't remember."

"Okay," I said agreeably.

Mrs. Livingston, I could tell, was a bit put out, but the main thing on her mind was buying the mask. Handing me a credit card she said, "Put it on my Visa."

I took the card and turned it over and over, staring at its golden surface as if it were an alien artifact.

"Is there something the matter with the card?" Mrs. Livingston asked.

"No, it's very pretty," I replied.

"Well, aren't you going to charge me?"

"Charge you for what?" I asked innocently.

"The mask."

"What mask?"

Mrs. Livingston was seriously annoyed now, but she wanted the mask so badly she went behind the desk, and ran the card through the machine herself. After signing the store copy and handing it to me, she said, "I'll be back to pick it up in an hour. Please have it well packed. By the way, where's your wife?"

"Of course," I said, smiling benignly.

As she was about to walk out the door, she turned to me and said, not unkindly, "Maybe you should lay off the *raicilla* for a while."

Raicilla was our local moonshine, a versatile beverage favored by plumbers (for unstopping drains), manicurists (for removing nail polish) and gardeners (for killing weeds).

"Nice to see you again, Mrs. Stanley," I said, waving bye-bye to her fleeing back.

A short while later three women entered the store, two of whom I recognized from previous visits. After greeting me effusively, they asked if they could use the ladies room.

"Of course," I said cooperatively.

"So, um, where is it?" one of the women asked.

"Home is where the heart is," I replied.

After utilizing the facilities, the three women, who were sisters, proceeded to buy out the shop, item after item: exquisitely hand-woven, hand-dyed wool rugs; the finest hand-painted Oaxacan animals; beautifully executed Talavera plates; and five pairs of choice silver earrings—all at our everyday low prices. While my assistant, Antonio, was packing everything up, one of the sisters paid me in cash. A little later Antonio returned, placing two large bags of merchandise atop the desk.

"That will be $5,575 pesos," I said to the sister in charge.

"Ha, ha," she said, "very funny."

"What do you mean?" I asked, my face a study in confusion.

"I already paid," she said, still chuckling, but beginning to look a little nervous.

"Paid for what?" I demanded.

"All of…this," she said, indicating the bags.

"All of this is yours?" I asked in amazement.

"Of course it's ours," she said, beginning to lose her temper.

"Are you sure?"

"Yes," she said, reaching for the bags, which I pulled protectively out of her reach.

"All right," I said reasonably, "if these are really yours, then you'll have to pay for them."

"But I already did," she insisted.

"Did what?"

At that, the three sisters went into a huddle in the corner. I could not make out most of what they said, but I did manage to catch the following: "…He doesn't *seem* drunk…Do you think he had an accident…He was fine the other day…"

Finally, I stood up, walked over to where they were standing and offered them the two bags of merchandise. "Excuse me," I said politely, "but do these bags belong to you?"

After they left, a man entered the shop and said to me, "Is Lucy here?"

"Lucy?" I said, frowning with concentration.

"Yes, you know, your wife," he said with a smile. "The woman who owns this shop."

"I'm married?" I asked in astonishment.

"So, she's not here?"

"Who?"

"Your wife!" the man shouted, finally losing his temper.

"I'm, I'm not sure," I mumbled nervously, opening and closing all the drawers in the desk, as if my wife might be hiding inside one.

The man, suddenly convinced that I was not joking, became alarmed. "Are you all right?" he asked.

"Sir," I said somberly, "may I ask you something?"

"Of course," he said with concern.

"Do I have children?"

"I...How should I know?"

"Well, you seem so knowledgeable," I said respectfully.

Just before lunchtime Mrs. Livingston returned to pick up her mask. As she approached the desk, I stood up, gave her my best smile and said, "Hello. May I help you?"

Peering at me suspiciously, she said, "Is my mask ready?"

Peering back at her with a look of equal suspicion, I said, "Ready for what?"

Mendoza Unchained

Why, I often ask myself, do small relatively crime-free Mexican cities like Puerto Vallarta require the services of fourteen separate law enforcement agencies? And how, in J. Edgar Hoover's name, do they decide who does what to whom?

After two decades of painstaking research into these deeply disturbing questions, I have arrived at several conclusions, many of them ominous. I now have reason to suspect, for example, that the Transit Police may in fact be restricted by law to dealing with traffic matters only, while the myriad other Law Enforcement agencies are proscribed from dealing with motor vehicles altogether! More or less.

In practical terms, I have absolutely no idea what this means, nor I suspect does anyone else. Except for Pete, a very regular customer at Steve's Bar, who told me that it was possible to run up to sixteen hundred red lights beneath the very noses of the Preventive, Municipal, Auxiliary, State, Federal, Tourist, Riot and Public Security Police Forces with little likelihood of receiving a ticket; while, conversely, committing non-vehicular acts of mayhem before the ever vigilant eyes of the traffic department will garner you nothing more than a stifled yawn.

On one of our recent shopping excursions to central Mexico, Lucy and I had the good fortune to witness a marvelous example of precisely the type of departmental separation of powers which Pete had been jabbering about.

We were sitting on a bench in the majestic colonial square in downtown Puebla eating ears of corn slathered with mayonnaise, cheese and chile, when a vehicular drama involving an illegally parked car unwound itself, like an episode of *Abbott and Costello*, right before our disbelieving eyes.

A couple from Mexico City had apparently parked their late-model vehicle too close to the corner, thereby obstructing access to the pedestrian crosswalk. They were away from their car for less than ten minutes (at a nearby ice-cream parlor), but that was long enough for the traffic police to go efficiently into action. By the time the gnomish middle-aged couple returned to their vehicle, a tow truck had already arrived upon the scene and attached itself proprietarily to their car. Even worse, a number of sticky paper seals had been affixed to all of the doors. These official seals are highly sacrosanct and may not be removed by *anyone* until the towed vehicle has been properly ransomed by its owner.

Needless to say the portly couple, blithely licking away the multi-hued carcinogenic sprinkles from the tops of their cones, were shocked sherbertless to learn that their vehicle had been assigned, sealed and all but delivered (by over a dozen traffic policepersons) to the impound lot— conveniently located somewhere in a nearby solar system.

Casting aside their cones, the outraged couple launched at once into a vigorous defense of their besieged vehicle. They had been gone only a few minutes! There was no sign indicating parking restrictions! They were being persecuted, etc., etc. None of these arguments had the least effect on the policemen, however, who proceeded to order the driver of the tow truck to mount his metal stallion and haul away.

As the driver started up the engine the defiant couple, hobbit-like in their fearlessness, went boldly into action; the husband inserting himself between the bumpers of the two vehicles and wrapping the slack chains of the tow truck around and around his arms, making it impossible for the truck to move without ripping his wrists off.

At the same time, his feisty wife, displaying a surprising agility for one so rotund, launched her own body across the hood, all the while screaming into a cell phone and giving everyone an excellent view of her hot-pink underwear. Then, slithering off the hood and risking heaven only knew what type of official reprisal, she brutally tore off one of the impound stickers, threw open the door and dove headfirst into the front seat, like Pete Rose stealing second base.

Informed by the ranking transit officer that they were committing serious criminal offenses, the husband and wife merely snarled back their defiance, egged on by a number of supporters in the rapidly growing crowd.

At this point I fully expected the couple to be arrested. But the traffic police, unable or unwilling to take any further action, were reduced to radioing the municipal police, who arrived *en force* forthwith.

As I sat removing several gobs of extraneous mayonnaise from my moustache, the crowd surrounding the impounded vehicle grew to seventy or more, counting the twoscore police persons and a lone hawker of lottery tickets, who was working the crowd with little success.

Lucy and I looked at each other.

"Who needs television," Lucy said.

Reaching into my daypack I pulled out a clipboard and rose purposefully to my feet.

"What are you doing?" Lucy asked fearfully.

"I'm going to poll the crowd," I replied.

"You mean, you're going to play reporter again?" she demanded disbelievingly.

"Of course. This is a golden opportunity."

"Don't you remember what happened the last time?"

"Don't worry; nothing will happen."

"How can you be sure?"

"I'll say I'm from Switzerland."

"Switzerland?"

Clipboard in hand I waded into the crowd and announced that I was a reporter from the *Zurich Zeitgeist*, and would anyone like to give an opinion about what was happening. Not surprisingly, almost everyone did.

There were, it quickly became apparent, two distinct camps. Those supporting the authorities all seemed to be of the opinion that *anyone* from Mexico City deserved to have his car towed, even if it was parked in his own garage. The other faction felt this all to be a gross case of official overreaction, and favored giving the poor couple a break.

"They were only parked there for a minute," a kindly man asserted. "The authorities should show some compassion and let them off with a small bribe."

"These *Chilangos* (a somewhat disparaging term for Mexico City residents) think they own the whole country," another fellow vociferated into my face. "They come here and park wherever they want; they eat in our restaurants; they throw garbage onto our…"

Suddenly, a team of Auxiliary Preventive Policepersons materialized out of nowhere, their objective, to unravel the tow chains from around the intractable husband's wrists. At the same time a female team from the same department began to haul the obstinate wife feet-first out of the front seat.

While the husband did everything in his power to make the disentangling process as tiresome as possible, his wife (wriggling and kicking) continued to scream at someone (her attorney, perhaps) on the cell phone.

Law enforcement personnel were now spontaneously generating all over the place. Fifty or more crowded around the semi-impounded vehicle. I decided to approach one of the transit policemen. "Could you tell me," I asked politely, "is it true that you are not empowered to arrest this couple?"

"That's correct," he replied with equal courtesy. "Interfering with the work of the Transit Police is not a traffic violation; it is a criminal violation and must be dealt with by a different agency."

"So that means," I asked, "that if an irate motorist were to punch you in the nose, you personally would not be able to arrest him?"

"That is correct."

"Amazing," I remarked. "But could you at least defend yourself?"

"Technically, yes and no," he replied uncertainly. "As I said, I would have to call a different agency."

"Such as?" I asked, my pen poised over the clipboard.

"Such as? Well, there's the Municipal Police, the Preventive Police, the Auxiliary Police, the Riot Police, the Anti-Riot Police, the State…"

Swim, But Don't Swallow

"Plagues," my neighbor Gertie informed me," always come in threes."

A gruff, nervy ex-New Yorker, Gertie had recently attained the Biblical age of eighty-two, so I had reason to believe she knew whereof she spoketh.

Casting an anxious eye out upon the rust-colored waters facing my home, I wondered if this, the *Red Tide*, could really be the first—of the three plagues, that is.

"You're not going to *swim* in that maritime *menudo*, are you?" Gertie demanded.

Swimming in the ocean was an indispensable part of my daily routine, and I was loathe to forgo it simply because a few gazillion fidoplankton (or whatever they were called) had turned the normally clear blue waters of Banderas Bay into a giant bowl of lobster bisque-gone bad.

"What makes you ask?" I muttered. I was fond of Gertie (in a perverse sort of way), but not when she was poking her big proboscis into my personal business.

"Well," she replied, leering levelly at my *Speedo*, "you've got a bathing suit on, for starters. If you can call that thing a bathing suit. To me it looks more like French underwear."

"I'm *thinking* of going swimming," I admitted.

"I thought you were intelligent," Gertie said with disappointment. "No genius, of course, but not a full-blown moron, either."

"Gertie, you're too kind."

"Can't you *smell* it?" she exploded.

In fact, I could smell it. "Yes," I allowed, "the ocean does smell a wee bit fishy today."

"Don't you mean, *dead*-fishy?" Gertie croaked disgustedly.

"Well..."

"Very, extremely dead-fishy!" Gertie snarled at my chest—on her best days the top of Gertie's head came nearly flush with my shoulder.

"All right, Gertie. If I do go swimming, I promise not to swallow any water."

With an expression of theatrical disbelief on her weathered face, my neighbor shouted, "What about your skin? Don't you even *care* about your skin?"

"Well, naturally I'll take a shower after..."

"No, forget your stupid skin." Gertie changed gears noisily, like an old sports car. "So you get a rash; you probably won't die from a rash— not even in this country. And, as you say, you'll keep your mouth shut, which would be a first. All well and good. But what I want to know is," she rumbled on, building to a hoarse, nasal New York crescendo, "what about the rest of them?"

"The rest of who?"

"Your *orifices*, you toadstool!"

"I'll keep my head out of the water," I swore.

"You can do that—swim with your head out of the water?"

"No problem."

"Even your ears?"

"Even my ears. Don't I hear Bernie calling you?" I asked hopefully.

Bernie was her husband, and he was not calling her. As a matter of fact, Bernie (who spent up to twelve hours a day watching *CNN*) rarely spoke aloud, especially to Gertie. In all the years we'd been neighbors I'd only known him to utter in his wife's presence a handful of phrases: "I'm hungry." "I'm tired." "Will you shut up, for Christ's sake!" And, in answer to her favorite query, "Yes, I moved my bowels today!"

"I doubt it," Gertie said. "At this hour he's either glued to the tube or to the toilet. Or both. Ever since we got that seven-inch job installed in the…"

I said, "Well I'm off," and stepped tentatively from the terrace onto the sand.

"You're really going swimming?"

"It looks that way."

"Just like that?"

"What do you mean?"

"I mean, without protection," Gertie said, staring pointedly (to my extreme discomfort) at my crotch.

"I don't follow you, Gertie."

"The human body has more orifices than meet the eye," she said enigmatically.

"I beg your pardon?"

Her next question, uttered with an amazing matter-of-factness, caught me completely off-guard. "Are you wearing a condom?" she demanded.

"To go swimming?"

"No, to play tennis," Gertie replied with raspy sarcasm.

"Well…I…Of course not," I sputtered stupidly. "I mean, that's the *Pacific Ocean* out there, Gertie. It's filled with fish, not table dancers!"

"Table dancers," Gertie repeated thoughtfully. "I've heard of them. Aren't they some new kind of *hoor* they've got?"

"Not exactly," I mumbled. "Well, I guess I'm off for my swim. See you…"

"Not so fast. So if they're not *hoors*, what are they? What do they do?"

"They're dancers, Gertie. They get up on tables and dance."

"And that's all?"

"Well no, that's not all," I said reluctantly. "Sometimes they get off the table and, uh, sit in your lap."

"And then what?" Gertie demanded aggressively, like the fat detective on *NYPD*. "I bet they do more than just sit there. I bet they squirm around like chickens."

"Chickens?"

"It seems to me," Gertie said suspiciously, "you know an awful lot about these new-fangled table prancing hoors. Is that where you're spending all your money while Lucy is away—getting squirmed on by some two-bit floozy? Your wife is a goddamn saint! You don't deserve her, and never did."

"You're right. I'm going swimming. See you…"

"Wait a minute. What about your butt? Bernie has some duct tape in his tool box. You ought to…"

I never heard what Gertie thought I should do with the duct tape in Bernie's toolbox, because I had already taken off at a gallop for the water.

Once immersed (up to my Adam's apple only) in the warm soothing ocean, I noticed two things: the water had a distinct slippery feel to it, and it was indeed infused to a disagreeable degree with the disturbing scent of aquatic decay. Nonetheless, I was soon paddling dutifully about with my neck ratcheted out to its maximum vertical extension (like a turtle) and my lips clamped tightly together, inhaling with the utmost caution through my nose.

Suddenly, the murky rust-colored water all around me was aboil with hundreds of small fish jumping repeatedly into the air, their fishy eyes wide with abject terror. Were they being perused by invisible predators, I wondered, or were they attempting to give their beleaguered orifices a temporary respite from the plankton-troubled waters?

Returning to the terrace I found Gertie grasping a garden hose with both hands and holding it at arm's length as if it were a venomous snake. Before she would allow me to enter my house, she insisted on hosing me down.

"But I'm going to take a shower," I protested.

"Good," she said, spraying me in the face. "Make sure you use lots of Clorox."

Before she succeeded in drowning me altogether, Bernie came shuffling double-time up to the terrace, his face convulsed with panic. "Haven't you been watching *CNN*?" he wheezed urgently. "There's a *Red Tide* on!"

"We know that, you dried-out couch potato," Gertie told her husband. "Go back to your stupid TV. And take another stool softener. You're so full of shit you're turning green."

The Frugal Vegetarian

B ruce was unnaturally thin, paler than an Eskimo's scrotum and dressed in clothes someone *had* been caught dead in. As he stood before my desk, he told me that he'd been in the shop a dozen times and couldn't understand why I did not remember him.

"I come into your shop every year," he said.

"How nice," I said, staring pointedly at my watch. "What can I do for you?"

"Don't you remember?" he persisted in an irritating nasal whine. "Three years ago you told me about a good vegetarian restaurant. It was very reasonable. I ate there every day."

Suddenly I did remember him: a rabid vegetarian who visited the store once a year for the sole purpose of grilling me about cheap new places to eat. Just the thought of consuming meat (or spending money) made him physically ill.

"Sorry," I said, "I still don't remember you. Are you sure you've been in here before?"

"Yes," Bruce said, an edge of exasperation creeping into his voice. "I told you, I come in here every year."

"So you've been in here, what, ten times?" I asked archly.

"At least," he said emphatically.

"And have you ever bought anything?"

"Well, I, uh, no," he admitted, taken momentarily by surprise. "But we always have such interesting discussions."

"Like we're having right now?"

Though apparently immune to feelings of shame or embarrassment, Bruce did pause for a moment to stare down at his disintegrating dollar twenty-nine flip-flops, which were leaving a trail of blue rubber crumbs on my freshly swept floor.

"Yes," he said with renewed purpose, "which reminds me; I was wondering if you could do me a small favor."

"For a terrific repeat-visitor like yourself, Bruce," I said expansively, "I'd crawl naked through a Turkish bathhouse."

"Oh, well, thanks," he said uncertainly. "What I'm interested in is that giant painted rooster sculpture you have in the window. It's the best I've ever seen. I'd love to own one."

"Bruce, you are a man of exceptional taste. Will that be cash or charge?"

"No, no," Bruce hurried to say. "I can't afford it, not at, you know, Vallarta prices."

"Vallarta prices?" I said. "This isn't exactly Beverly Hills, Bruce."

"I know, but I'm on a budget right now. So I was wondering if you could tell me how to get hold of the artist who made it so I could buy one directly from him."

"Directly from him?"

"Yes, you know," Bruce explained, "eliminate the middleman."

"The middleman?" I repeated with a hurt expression on my face. "That's me, Bruce. Are you saying that you want to eliminate *me*? You know, I'm a person, too, Bruce—not some byproduct of a bowel movement you can just flush down the toilet and forget about. I have feelings, Bruce. I have…"

"Sorry, I didn't mean it like that," Bruce said. "I was just hoping you could help me find the artist. I'd really like to meet him."

"Oh, that's different," I said graciously. "Sure, no *problema*. Pull up a chair."

"Thanks," he said, beaming with anticipation.

"Well, let me tell you, Bruce, this fellow lives in kind of a rural area; no phones for miles around."

"Then how do you contact him?"

"I go and see him in person."

"Okay," he said, "I can do that. How do I find his house?"

"Well, that's a bit involved. You might want to make some notes."

"I was planning to," he said with a broad grin, whipping out a pad of unlined paper and a plastic pen.

"Do they sell it cheaper that way, Bruce?"

"Sell what cheaper?"

"The pad of paper; is it cheaper without the lines?"

"Oh...I'm not really sure."

"Okay, Bruce, the first thing you do is you drive to Guadalajara."

"How long does that take?" he asked, pen poised over the pad.

"That depends," I said.

"On what?"

"On whether or not you get stuck behind a pig truck. Besides slowing you down, it can be a pretty nasty experience. You don't eat pork, do you?"

"No, I'm a vegetarian. I'm opposed to eating flesh of any kind."

"That's good," I said, "because after driving behind one of those pig trucks, you'd never be able to eat pork again."

"Yes, yes," Bruce said impatiently, "so how long will it take?"

"Okay, if you get stuck behind a pig truck, which you probably will—and let me tell you, the smell is something you'll *never* forget. Those poor pigs, they've got them wedged into these cages for days, and they're making poo-poo and pee-pee and God only knows what all over them..."

"If you don't mind, I'd rather not hear about this," Bruce said with a pained expression on his face.

"Sorry. It's just that after getting stuck behind a pig truck once, I couldn't eat ribs for a month. And I *love* ribs: short ribs, spare ribs, long..."

"How many hours is it?" Bruce barked.

"About five."

"And his address in Guadalajara?"

"Oh, he doesn't live in Guadalajara," I said regretfully.

"He lives outside of town then?"

"In a manner of speaking. So from Guadalajara, you get on Highway 95 and follow the signs for Mexico City."

"For how long?"

"About six hours. Now, once you've driven across Mexico City, which can take anywhere from forty-five minutes to a month, depending on whose demonstrating that day—if it's the Teacher's Union, then you're going to have a real..."

"*Across* Mexico City?"

"Yes."

"But, but where *is* this place?"

"Oaxaca," I replied. "Once you're past Mexico City, you've got it made; then it's only another seven hours to Oaxaca City, if you take the toll roads, which can be expensive, but which provide the traveler with a degree of security, comfort and convenience that more than makes up for the additional cost."

"Yes, yes, I understand. So what is his address in Oaxaca?"

"Well, he's not actually *in* Oaxaca, Bruce. But we're practically there. Shall I keep going?"

"Yes," he said, gritting his teeth.

"Okey-dokey. So. You drive out of Oaxaca City, going west, for exactly seventeen kilometers. Then you turn left onto a dirt road. You'll know it's the right road because there's a taco stand on every corner. Beef, I'm afraid. Okay, so you go about thirteen hundred meters down the dirt road, or until you come to a green pickup truck. Then you turn right and..."

"Wait a minute. What if the truck's not there?"

"Oh, it's almost always there," I assured him.

"But what if it's not?"

"In that case, if I were you, I'd just pull over and take a nap or something, because you'll never find the place without the truck as a landmark."

"This seems unnecessarily complicated," he complained.

"Just like life in general, Bruce. That's what my Philosophy 101 professor used to say whenever we got into one of those discussions about how could there be a loving and compassionate God when life was so filled with strife and suffering. Professor Mendelbaum—that was his name—first he'd say, 'God, why have you, who are supposed to be all-merciful, created disease and pain and hunger?' Then Professor Mendelbaum would answer his own question, as if *he* were *God*. He'd say, 'So, who said it was going to be easy?' The whole class would crack up then, because the professor sounded just like Zero Mostel in *Fiddler On The Roof*. You remember, that Broadway show about…"

"Yes, yes, yes," Bruce growled. "So, I'm at the green truck. Now what?"

"Okay, so you turn right, onto a gravel road, which turns into a dirt road, and then into no road at all. But don't worry. Just keep driving until you can't go any further. Then you'll see a large meadow filled with cows. But they're only dairy cows," I added quickly, "so you don't have to worry about anyone eating them."

"I don't consume dairy products of any kind," the extreme vegetarian declared fiercely.

"Well, at your age," I remarked sensibly, "you probably don't need them. You'll find three separate trails traversing the meadow—if it hasn't been raining; sometimes they get washed out in the rain. Take the trail on the left and keep walking for about four miles, or until you come to a tree stump."

"A *tree stump*?"

"That's correct. Turn right at the stump and after a while you'll come to a small goat ranch. They'll probably want you to try one of their barbecued baby goats, but all you have to do is explain that you're a vegetarian and they'll give you some rice and beans instead."

"I don't speak Spanish."

"Oh. Well then, just use sign language. You know, point at the goat, then at your mouth, then make the sign of the cross or something. Now, anybody at the ranch can tell you how to get to Jose's house, so..."

"Jose is the sculptor?" Bruce asked hopefully.

"No, Jose is his wife's brother. But they're very close. When they were kids, Jose almost drowned, but his wife's brother, whose name escapes me at the moment—Mario, or Manuel, or Miguel, or...Bruce? Bruce, where are you going? We've just got a veal scaloppini factory to get past and we're home free."

My Shoes, My Shoes

Within hours of moving into our comfy but dilapidated beach house we were bedeviled by so many phone calls I was tempted to call in an exorcist.

Apparently, every human being not chained to the walls of a dungeon or encased inside an iron lung was suddenly planning to pay us a visit. There were brothers, sisters, old friends, new friends, mothers-in-law, uncles, aunts and several people who, quite frankly, we had never even heard of—all of them unable to resist the allure of staying rent-free in a beachfront house in Puerto Vallarta.

"How am I going to get any work done?" I complained to my wife. "We've got to trim the fat; cut back; outsource these freeloaders to Mazatlan!"

"All right," Lucy said agreeably, "who do you suggest we do away with first?"

"How about your Uncle Lupe?"

"No way; I love Uncle Lupe."

"Well then, what about eliminating his wife; she's not even related to you."

"Lupe's wife is not negotiable," Lucy stated flatly.

After several hours of discordant dialogue, we agreed to accept everyone belonging to Lucy's gene pool, my cousin Lenny and two old friends from California. The mystery couple, who allegedly met us at a chili cook-off five years ago, we politely told to take a hike.

Time passed. And passed. And passed.

Eight weeks later the flood of house guests had largely subsided, leaving us exhausted, sun burnt, nearly broke and desperately in need of a vacation ourselves.

"Well," I told Lucy, as we sat bleary-eyed and shell-shocked, sharing a rare private moment on the terrace, "it's just ten days of your mom, and then we're home-free till next year."

"And you don't mind my mom, right?" Lucy asked.

"Of course not. Connie is my favorite mother-in-law."

Connie was also *very* respectful of my need for peace and quiet, going out of her way not to make any noise whatsoever while I was writing.

"I'm glad you and my mom get along so well," Lucy said. "It's a good indication."

"A good indication of what?"

"A good indication that you'll get along with her friends, too."

"Her *what*?"

"Didn't I tell you? She's bringing two friends along. For company."

"*Company*?" I said a trifle too loud. "What does she need company for? What's wrong with us?"

"She wanted to have someone her own age around."

"You mean," I moaned with panic, "she's bringing two seventy-year-old women with her?"

"No," Lucy said, tensing her thighs for flight, "they're a little older than her. Gladys, I think, is seventy-five. And Dorothy is turning eighty, or eighty-seven—I can't remember. Honey," she added, eyeing me fearfully, "you're grinding your teeth again. You know what the dentist said."

At four o'clock the following afternoon my wife began to install into our congested home Connie, Gladys and Dorothy, who between them had brought along enough equipment to mount an invasion of North Korea. The three women were going to cohabitate (sorority-style) our solitary guest bedroom, utilizing a combination of cots, foldout beds and disposable hammocks. Their bags, meanwhile, lay heaped on the living room floor, forming a small mountain around which I was compelled to tip-toe sideways.

Dorothy, who had already mistaken me for two of her deceased husbands, suddenly grew frantic; she had, apparently, misplaced her favorite shoes.

Soon a house-wide hunt was underway for the mysteriously missing footwear, a search in which I refused to participate. I had, in fact, retired to my bedroom, closed the door and begun to make a mental inventory of places I could move to where no one would want to visit me. Topping the list was Devil's Island, followed closely by the Gobi Desert, Northern Greenland and Newark, New Jersey.

"She thinks she left her shoes at the airport," Lucy said, bursting into the bedroom.

"That's nice," I said. "Honey, I've been thinking, too. Maybe moving to the beach wasn't such a good idea. Maybe we should live someplace a little more tranquil. Like a subway station. Or a high school cafeteria. Or a crack house!" I concluded energetically.

Before Lucy could reply, Dorothy herself shuffled inside.

"What's that terrible noise?" she inquired. "It sounds like a steamroller."

"That's the ocean, Dorothy," Lucy patiently explained. "You know, the sound of the waves breaking on the beach?"

"Well, get somebody to turn it down," Dorothy demanded. "It's giving me a headache!"

"I'll get on it right away," I assured her.

Pacified for the moment, Dorothy stood staring calmly off into space for a while. Then...

"My shoes, my shoes, I can't find my shoes!" she exclaimed. "I must have left them at the airport."

"That seems kind of unlikely, Dorothy," I said.

"Then they stole them out of my luggage," Dorothy declared. "I have to get them back. They're the only pair that goes with my white shorts."

"Uh, Dorothy," I said, "could you do me a small favor, please?"

"Yes? Yes?" she said frantically.

"Could you take a look at your feet for a moment and tell me what you see?"

"My shoes!" she screeched with glee. "I've found my shoes!"

"Come on, Dorothy," Lucy said, gently leading her out of the bedroom, "we better call *Interpol* and let them know they can open the borders again."

Los Tules is one of the most beautiful resorts in Mexico, what with its lush tropical gardens, half-kilometer of beach and eye-pleasing architecture. The manager of the resort, Carlos Rentacuarto, was a good friend and, more importantly, he owed me several favors. Calling him on the phone, I explained my problem.

"Can you help me out, Carlos?" I asked him.

Carlos said he could and promised to provide me, "almost free", with a two-bedroom ocean-front condo. My only problem now was how to relocate Gladys and Dorothy gracefully, disguising the unattractive fact that I was in reality giving the multi-genarians the old heave-ho. For the sake of verisimilitude, I left the house for a few hours, taking a long walk along the beach. When I returned, amazingly enough, everyone was still engaged in the monumental task of sorting out the hillock of luggage.

"Dorothy! Gladys!" I shouted excitedly. "You aren't going to believe what happened!"

"What happened?" Gladys asked.

"Did you find my shoes?" Dorothy demanded.

"You two ladies have got to be the two luckiest women in Puerto Vallarta!" I proclaimed.

"Puerto Vallarta?" Dorothy said uncertainly.

"What is it?" Gladys asked, her eyes aglitter.

"The other day," I explained, "I entered you into a contest. And you both won first place. Congratulations!"

"What kind of contest?" Lucy asked suspiciously.

"It was," I replied, shooting my wife a warning look, "the *Name the New McDonald's* contest."

"Name the new..." my mother-in-law began.

"And," I interrupted her, "guess what you two incredibly privileged people have won."

"What? What?"

"A free nine-day stay in the most luxurious two-bedroom condominium in Puerto Vallarta!"

"Puerto Vallarta?" Dorothy said again.

"Oh! Oh! Oh!" Gladys chirped with excitement. "It's my dream come true—a luxury condominium!"

"A luxury condom?" Dorothy said. "Is that good? I think my third husband had one."

"You bet, Dorothy. Let's get your bags loaded up, girls. The offer expires in twenty minutes."

On the way over to *Los Tules* Gladys asked me, "So what was the name?"

"What name?" I asked cheerfully.

"The name you submitted for the new *McDonald's*."

"Oh, right, the name. It was, uh, let me think..."

"*McDonald's!*" Dorothy exclaimed. "*That's* where I left my shoes!"

Cabin Beaver

For the first forty-five minutes the flight had been strictly routine: the useless emergency instructions, the miniature bag of salted peanuts, the half-glass of reanimated orange juice and the promise of an ice-cold "something and cheese" sandwich to be dumped upon the foldout somewhere over Cabo San Lucas. Then, at minute forty-six, I rose to use the restroom.

I have always despised airplane bathrooms and use them as infrequently as possible. The overpowering odor of disinfectant, the cramped quarters and the inevitable "small pockets of turbulence" always combine to make me nauseous. So anxious was I on this occasion to put my ordeal (making *numero dos*) behind me that I committed, in my claustrophobic haste, an act of airlineal indiscretion: hitting the flush button while still enthroned.

Then I attempted to stand up, and to my unconditional dismay, I could not. After several further futile attempts, the terrible truth hit me with the force of a shrieking kamikaze: My ass was, like a can of *Folger's* coffee, vacuum-sealed to the toilet seat!

Hard upon this horrifying realization came an announcement from the wee speaker over the door advising everyone to return to their seats. Several minutes after that a stewardess named Lenore came rapping on the restroom door.

"Sir? Madam?" she called out authoritatively. "Could you please return to your seat? We are about to experience some minor turbulence."

"Well," I said to the door, "I would very much like to return to my seat, but I'm afraid I cannot."

"Why not? Are you all right, sir?"

"All right in what sense?"

"Do you need a doctor?"

"No, I don't think so. Not yet."

Actually, I wasn't sure what I needed. Was there a word for a person whose job is to separate people's buttocks from the toilet seats of airplanes? Probably not.

"What seems to be the problem, then?" the stewardess asked impatiently.

"Apparently, I have become stuck to the seat," I replied urbanely.

"*Stuck to the seat?*"

"That's what I said, dear."

"What do you mean?"

"Well," I explained with didactic precision, "it would seem that, by activating the flush mechanism prematurely, I have created what is known as a vacuum seal."

"You flushed while you were still on the potty?" she demanded in a loud voice.

"Affirmative."

"You're not supposed to do that," she scolded.

"No kidding."

"He flushed while he was still on the potty!" she shouted at someone.

"He did *what*?"

"Now he's stuck. He can't get up."

"I'll tell the captain."

The predicted buffeting began at that moment, and I heard no more from the crew for quite a while. During this turbulent time, though the rest of my body was jarred this way and that, my *gluteus maxima* (super-glued to the stainless steel seat) refused to budge even a micron. Then a commanding male voice addressed me from the other side of the door.

"This is Captain Conrad speaking," the voice announced. "Are you all right in there, sir?"

"More or less, Captain."

"Are you experiencing any breathing difficulties?" he asked.

For several moments I stared at the door, wondering if Captain Conrad was pulling my leg. "*Breathing?*" I finally said.

"Do you have a heart condition, or any other health issues we need to know about?" the Captain inquired.

"No, Captain, I'm as sound as a government bond," I announced proudly.

"Your circulation is good, sir?"

"Well, now that you mention it, my feet are starting to fall asleep. But that's not what worries me," I added darkly.

"Listen," the Captain said, "have you tried, ah, you know, squirming, sir, twisting…ah…"

"Captain, I've tried everything but the Boogaloo. Can't *you* do something?"

"That's a negative, sir. We can't open the door from the outside. You're just going to have to hang tough until we land."

"What about my whatever and cheese sandwich?" I cried, but the Captain had gone.

For the next half hour I was left alone with my thoughts, which were largely black and revolved around the growing certainty that long before the plane landed in San Francisco, I was going to lose my gonads to gangrene. Desperate to distract myself I tried to think of something intelligent I'd done recently. This proved to be more difficult than I'd hoped. But then my mind alit upon the wonderfully clever manner in which I had solved the "Christmas Gift Dilemma".

Since I resided in Mexico I was expected, upon my infrequent visits to California, to schlep along presents for several dozen assorted friends and relations. Naturally, travelling by air (post 9/11) with twenty-four unique Mexican gifts can present the passenger with any number of awkward problems. But I had solved them all by acquiring two dozen beautifully handcrafted miniatures at *Lucy's Cucu Cabaña*, one of the finest folk-art shops in the Western Hemisphere. They had all fit snugly into a single standard shoebox and, to cap it off, my wife had given me a terrific deal.

"This is the Captain speaking," my little speaker drawled. "Some of the passengers have been requesting information as to why one of our rear lavatories has been placed, ah, off-limits. Well, let me assure you that there is absolutely no cause for alarm. It seems that one of our passengers, a Mr. Gevins, who resides in Puerto Vallarta, by the way, did something rather, ah, *creative*. He, ah, ha, ha—this is a little hard to believe, folks—he, ah, flushed while he was still, ah, sitting down, and has become stuck to the, ah, seat."

Once the cabin-wide peals of laughter had subsided, the Captain, barely managing to contain his own mirth, went on with his announcement. "I've been flying commercial airliners for almost twenty years, and I, ah, must say this is the first time I've even *heard* of something like this happening. So, if you see me wandering every now and then to the, ah, *rear* of the plane, you'll know why. By the way, if those of you on the starboard side of the cabin look quickly to your left, you'll be treated to a truly spectacular view of the, ah, Pacific Ocean. It really is, ah, quite blue today."

Ten minutes later Captain Conrad came knocking once again on the door of my vertical coffin. "You all right in there?"

"You mean," I hissed with venom, "have I died of embarrassment yet?"

"Listen," he began placatingly, "you know nowadays passengers are always a little nervous so…"

"Thanks for announcing my name," I interrupted him. "Too bad you didn't have a photograph; you could have passed that around, too, along with my e-mail directory."

"Hey, keep your pants on…I mean, please remain calm, sir. There's nothing we…"

"Do you know what a lawsuit is, Captain?"

"Ah, listen, Mr. Gevins, there's no need to, ah…"

"How much," I cut in, "do you suppose a pair of reasonably functioning human testicles are worth on the open market these days, Captain?"

"Mr. Gevins, please lower your voice. You're going to alarm the other passengers."

"Alarm the *other passengers*?" I screamed. "What about me? I'm being neutered by a *fucking toilet seat*!"

"All right," the Captain said in his soothing pilot's baritone, "I understand. I feel your pain. Let me assure you: Everything is going to be fine. I've radioed ahead to my superiors and they have informed me that our *Rest Room Evacuation Team* is already on alert. And once you are, ah, detached from your present predicament, you will be absolutely *swimming* in frequent-flier miles."

I, Mermaid

Last week a rotund woman, who for some reason reminded me of an enormous pigeon, stutter-stepped into my wife's shop and, without preamble, made the following series of breathless declarations: "I have a friend. She really likes your store. She says you have great mermaids. I love mermaids. I need to use the bathroom."

Several minutes later she emerged from said chamber still declaiming: "That is a very clean bathroom. I'm impressed. You're to be congratulated. I want to buy some mermaids."

"Of course," I said graciously. "Please allow me to show you a few of my personal favorites."

"Oh, thank you so much!" she trilled.

"All right," I began, "first we have our flying papier-mâché mermaids—wings optional."

"I love them!" she cooed.

"Then we have these delightful hand-molded, hand-painted, naïve ceramic mermaid Christmas tree ornaments."

"They're wonderful!" she cried.

"Yes," I admitted, "almost as wonderful as our painted Betty Boop mermaids, our coconut mermaids, our painted wood mermaids, and our transsexual mermaids, which are only rivaled by..."

"Transsexual?" the woman warbled.

"Yes," I said proudly, "here at *Lucy's Cucu Cabaña*, 'Trans-Gender Chic' is the order of the day. Then we have our tin mermaids, our copper mermaids, our..."

And on and on I droned until I had all but enumerated myself to sleep.

"My name is Clarice," the woman said, offering me her hand, which bore upon it enough rings to short-circuit an airport metal detector.

"Clarice, Clarice, what a lovely name," I crooned. "You're not a Jodie Foster fan, are you?"

"Jodie Foster?"

"You know," I said helpfully, "Agent Starling? Hannibal the Cannibal?"

"No, I don't know," Clarice said, eyeing me uncertainly. "Are there any mermaids I haven't seen yet?"

"Oh, yes!" I enthused. "Last but not least, we have our full-length, authentic ceremonial Mermaid Costume, made and danced by the Nahuatl Indians in the highlands of *Lower Netzahualcoyotl*."

At the sight of the life-sized, painted canvas suit with its simple but tastefully carved mermaid mask, Clarice became quite lively, bouncing up and down like a springless pogo stick. "I have to have it!" she chirped five or six times. "Tell me about the mask."

"The mask," I explained, "is carved from the wood of the sacred *Zompontle* tree. Well into the early twentieth century this tree was prized by the colorful Indian Shamans for its bright red psychotropic seeds, which when ingested would put them into a deep and colorful trance."

When I had concluded my exposition, Clarice became very quiet.

"You seem like a fairly open-minded person," she said after a long pause.

"Clarice, I am as open as they come. In fact, some of my best friends are people I can't stand."

"May I share something with you?" Clarice asked in a soft conspiratorial tone.

"As long as it's not a communicable disease," I replied bravely, "fire away."

"I'm a mermaid," she cooed confidentially.

"No kidding?" I said, reaching for the stun gun I kept against just such a contingency in the drawer of my desk.

"Do you think," Clarice asked anxiously, "I could try on the costume?"

When I hesitated, she said huffily, "I'm definitely buying it, if you're concerned about any potential damage I might do. Here's my credit card."

"It's not that, Clarice," I said, swiping the card through the terminal so fast it left a small cloud of smoke in its wake. "The costume is rather abrasive. And the mask—it's going to be really rough on that delicate skin of yours."

"So how did the Indian Shamans manage?" Clarice asked. "Didn't they dance in it for hours at a time?"

"You have to understand, Clarice," I explained patiently, "these Shamans were not ordinary men. They buried themselves alive for days on end. They stuck long ugly thorns through indelicate portions of their personal physiognomies. They spent weeks at a time watching *Jerry Springer* reruns. And they ate those magical red seeds which, from what I understand, taste absolutely terrible. In other words, Clarice, they were a pretty tough bunch of dudes."

"Magical seeds!" Clarice tweeted. "I'd love to see some."

"You happen to be in luck. We sell bracelets made entirely of those red seeds, and here they are."

"Oh, they're fun!" Clarice exclaimed, putting one on.

"Yes, and far more comfortable than that scratchy suit," I pointed out.

"Do you have a dressing room?" she asked.

"We have a bathroom," I admitted warily.

Ten minutes later Clarice stumbled stiffly from the bathroom wearing the entire authentic Mermaid Costume, which on the one hand fit her surprisingly well, but on the other looked unspeakably strange, especially with all those wads of blond hair leaping out from behind the wooden mask.

"It is a little uncomfortable," her muffled voice informed me.

"Clarice, you look absolutely marvelous!" I exclaimed.

Removing the mask, she said, "I'll take five of those bracelets, as well."

"Of course," I said, hurrying to wrap up the entire transaction before something untoward occurred.

"Don't wrap up the bracelets," Clarice advised me, "I'm going to eat some of them right now."

"What?"

"I want to enter a Shamanic trance," she declared. "How far is it to the beach?"

"No, no, no, Clarice, I don't think that's a very good idea."

"Why not? Is the water polluted?"

"No, the water is fine. It's just that...Clarice, do you mind if I ask you a question?"

"No, go ahead."

"What exactly," I asked with trepidation, "are your immediate intentions vis-à-vis the authentic Mermaid Costume, the magical red seeds and the beach?"

"What do you mean?" she asked. "What are you afraid of?"

My fear, which I dared not put into words, was that Clarice, after eating one or more bracelets, was going to catch a cab to *Los Muertos* Beach and, still wearing the authentic full-length Mermaid Costume, jump off the pier.

"Clarice," I said gently, "you can't eat those bracelets."

"Why not? You said the Shamans ate them."

"Yes, that is what I've been told, Clarice, but you must understand that ingesting those bracelets may do a great deal more than put you into a trance."

"Are you talking about ego-loss?"

"Well..."

"Ego-loss does not frighten me," Clarice asserted. "After all, I survived the Sixties."

That's a matter of opinion, I thought.

"Clarice, it is very possible that those seeds are toxic," I carefully explained, "as well as being psychotropic; often the two go together. Terrible things could happen if you eat them: you could die; you could suffer brain damage;

you could even wind up spending the rest of your vacation *sitting on the potty!*"

But Clarice refused to heed my advice and the next morning the front page of our English-language daily sported the following banner headline: FINLESS FLIPPED-OUT FOREIGNER FOUND FLOUNDERING IN FIVE INCHES OF WATER!

Advantage, Victim

Visitors to our fair seaside city are always asking me if Vallarta is a safe place to live. My reply is invariably in the affirmative, but I do add a caveat: PV is a safe place, but it is not *Disneyland!* Then I proceed to tell them, if they have a few hours to kill, about how, over the past twenty years, my home has been the site of three botched burglaries.

Blundered break-in number one occurred in the summer of 1983 at our first house on Basilio Badillo. Lying awake on a sweltering August night, I spied the pint-sized pirate poking his head tentatively inside our bedroom door. For some time I'd been sleeping (due to reports of a cat burglar in the neighborhood) with a dangerously oversized monkey wrench under my pillow. Grabbing this inelegant weapon, I leapt to my feet and set off, naked and screaming, in humid pursuit.

Fortunately for the both of us, he was a quick little bugger and managed to hop the front gate just ahead of me. As the frightened felon took off down the street, I began to pound on the locked metal door with my humongous wrench, howling all the while with animal rage.

Regretfully, there were no attractive young women about at that hour to appreciate this magnificent spectacle. Only my wife, from the bedroom balcony, had observed my savage display in all its earsplitting eye-pleasing glory.

"I didn't know you had it in you, honey," she sighed, her eyes aglow with admiration. "It was just like watching *Planet of the Apes.*"

When I'd calmed down somewhat I noticed that the young man had, in his rush to escape my B-movie wrath, left behind a pair of tennis shoes.

Advantage, Victim.

A full decade later, when we were living across town in our old beach house, bollixed break-in number two took place. We'd been working late at the shop and must have arrived home only minutes after the miniature malefactor had squeezed through a high small window we'd always deemed impregnable. Only later did we did notice the broken screen and the absence of an old pair of my tennis shoes, which the midget must have run right into as he scampered out the back door.

Score: Fifteen-All.

(In all fairness to my adopted home, and in order to insulate myself from any potential problems with the *Powers-That-Be*, I should probably point out, parenthetically, that break-ins are relatively rare occurrences in our tranquil beachside resort, and even three measly incidents over a twenty-year span is, according to the meticulously kept records of the *DRD—Department of Revolting Developments—* far in excess of the Two-Decade Moving Average.)

Having thus covered my scrawny white behind, it is my sad duty to report that...

Eight years later, we were struck again.

This third violation of our personal space occurred while we were still living in the beach house, which unbeknownst to everyone (with the possible exception of Shirley MacLaine) was only seven months shy of being smashed to smithereens by a forty-foot wave.

Lucy was leaving the house a little after nine pm, locking behind her the gate to our dark lonely driveway, when she was approached by a young man wearing a blue baseball cap, who proceed to ask her—not impolitely—for money.

"You want money?" Lucy asked him, as she climbed back into her car.

"Yes," he said.

"Then let me see some ID," she demanded unexpectedly.

Most likely we will never know if this particular person had ever been asked to produce his identification before. But it is fairly safe to assume that this was the first time in his life that he had received such a request from an American woman sitting in a Volkswagen Bug on a dark street between the hours of nine and ten pm.

Open-mouthed, immobilized and mute, he stood there staring in disbelief at my wife, until she floored the gas and popped the clutch, leaving the young man lost in a cloud of salty dust.

I arrived home two hours later. I'd been working the nightshift at the shop, while my slave-driver wife was out carousing with her girlfriends. Nothing seemed to be amiss as I unlocked the front door. But then I heard a loud metal clanging sound emanating from the back porch, which sent me instantly into one of my patented "chimp-fits". Bounding into the living room, I saw that our badly rusted backdoor had been twisted partially off its hinges. By the time I had squeezed through the narrow opening and sprung, with simian agility, out onto the beach, the intruder was gone. Grabbing a lead pipe with one hand and the phone with the other, I called the police.

While I waited for them to arrive I attempted in vain to discover what if anything was missing. The house, it turned out, was largely unscathed, except for the bedroom where the contents of all the drawers had been dumped onto the floor and several cushions had been slashed open, their stuffing littering the room like clumps of gray cotton candy.

Looking grim and toting a pair of enormous shotguns, two bullet-proof-vested policemen arrived on the scene in record time. After a short three-way chat, we began to search for clues. First we found, just outside the mangled door, an old pair of tennis shoes and a blue baseball cap, neither of which belonged to me, forcing us to the ineluctable conclusion that they must have belonged to the thief. Then we discovered some tracks in the sand (made, the policemen cannily concluded, by a pair of *Nike* athletic shoes) leading in the direction of the vacant house next door.

While I guarded the fort, my knights in bulletproof armor went off to investigate, returning five minutes later with Pablo, the *velador*. Pablo was pushing eighty, but looked even older. He'd been hired to stay awake all night and keep an eye on the empty house.

"Here's your burglar," the policemen told me.

"But he's the *velador*," I said. "What makes you think *he* did it?"

"Three things," the taller of the two officers replied shrewdly. "First, he's wearing *Nikes*, and the tracks leading away from your house were made by *Nikes*."

"What else?"

"We smelled shampoo on that baseball cap, and this guy's head smells like he just washed his hair with the same shampoo, *Almond Nectar*."

"And?"

"And when we found him he was pretending to be asleep in a hammock. Once he was 'awake', I put my hand on his chest and I could feel his heartbeat racing out of control. Obviously, he was nervous."

Nervous? After being rousted in the middle of the night by two men who looked like they were about to invade Guatemala? It was a miracle old Pablo hadn't had a heart attack!

"And that's *it*?" I demanded in disbelief. "*Nikes*, nervous and *Almond Nectar*?"

"That's enough for us," he replied grimly. "We're taking him in."

"I have to tell you," I said, eyeing Pablo (who would have had difficulty opening the terrace door *with a key*), "I have my doubts. To me this looks like the work of a much younger man."

"Some of these old geezers are stronger than they look," he opined.

Then the two policemen turned around and, without a backward glance, led the clean-haired, *Nike*-shod, nervous old watchman away.

My wife returned home just after one. I told her we'd been robbed and we began to sift through the ruins of the bedroom.

"The only thing that seems to be missing," she announced finally, "are my aerobic shoes."

"*Nikes*?"

Lucy nodded. "We're lucky that's all he got."

"Thanks to you," I beamed with husbandly pride.

"What do you mean?"

"Well, the way I see it, every time the thief opened one of these drawers, he was confronted by the tons of junk you've been accumulating for the last twenty years, and apparently it drove him insane, which must be why he started cutting open cushions, instead of looking under the bed where all the money was."

"You see?" Lucy said. "There was a method to my messiness after all. And to think, you've been bugging me forever to throw all that stuff away!"

"Yes," I admitted, "I've been a fool."

Standing there amid the chaos of the ransacked room we held each other close and gave silent thanks for our good fortune.

"Hey, guess what," I said. "It just occurred to me: We lost one pair of tennis shoes, but acquired another. So we're still tied with the burglars: Thirty-All. We're even up a baseball cap!"

"Was it a blue baseball cap?" Lucy asked.

In no time at all I was in direct telephonic communication with the Comandante himself to whom I explained the entire situation.

"My men are pretty sure they got the right man," he said when I'd finished giving him the facts.

"But my wife *saw* the burglar," I insisted. "He was only twenty years old. The *velador* is almost eighty. And he couldn't have bent that iron door; he can barely open a jar."

"Well, all right," the Comandante said reluctantly. "We'll release the suspect in the morning, as soon as you come in to make a statement."

It was my turn to work the shop, so the next morning Lucy drove out to the jail to do our civic duty. After stating her business she was ushered into a small dingy room where a neatly dressed man sat at a wooden desk, his manicured fingers poised over the keys of an enormous manual typewriter.

"How many square meters is your terrace?" the interviewer asked her.

"What?"

"The dimensions of the terrace where the door was broken—what are they?"

"I have no idea."

"Take a guess."

"I don't know," Lucy said, "forty meters?"

"That's an awfully big terrace," the man said accusatorily.

"Yes, I suppose it is," Lucy agreed.

"And the property, how many square meters is that?"

"I really don't know," Lucy said, "and what does that have to do with…"

"These are required questions," the man said. "If you don't answer them, we can't prosecute the suspect."

"You mean you caught him already?"

"Caught who already?"

"The kid who broke into the house."

"I have no idea," the man replied, "that is not my department. Are you married?"

"Yes, but…"

"How many years?"

"Eighteen," Lucy replied, "but I don't see…"

"How many children?"

"No children."

"Why not?" he demanded.

"What?"

"Why don't you have any children? Is there something wrong with your husband?" the official asked with an insinuating leer. "If there is, maybe we could work something out."

"I don't think so," Lucy said, rising from her chair.

"Why not?"

"It's a matter of legumes," she said.

"Legumes?"

"Yes," my wife explained as she gathered up her purse. "Men like you, with pea-sized brains and peanut-sized penises, have never been my cup of tea. Have a nice day."

Why a Duck?

Among the many things for which I have little or no patience, waiting in line at the bank heads the list. Which is why I do my banking at *Bancomal*. They have a 'Take-a-Number" system, allowing me to relax outside in Vallarta's picturesque square while the torturous count-up to my turn crawls painfully forward.

On the morning in question I had drawn number ninety-seven. The bank's digital display was lit up by a big fifty-nine. With a little luck I'd be cashing my check sometime the following week.

And so, ticket in hand I exited the bank in search of a shady place to plant my posterior for a while. But shade was in short supply and the only suitably sitable spot was in imminent danger of being occupied by an exhausted-looking woman with a cane.

Weary though she may have been, the woman seemed disinclined to sit down. The cause of her reluctance, I saw, was a large black Labrador who sat tied by his leash to one end of the bench.

"Excuse me," I said politely, "but were you going to sit on this bench?"

"Yes," she said, "but I'm afraid of the dog. He looks mean."

The big drooling Lab did not look mean to me. He looked, in fact, like the biggest pushover in the state of Jalisco.

"That's a Labrador," I said, showing off my extensive knowledge of the canine kingdom. "They're among the friendliest, nicest dogs in the world."

"But he's so big," she shuddered. "What if he decides to attack me?"

"Labradors don't attack people," I laughed. "Watch this."

And then I did something I'd done dozens of times before—which did not make it any less stupid. I jammed my wrist into the dog's mouth. "See, I told the woman, "this big fellah is totally harmless."

"Is he your dog?" she asked suspiciously.

"No, I've never seen him before."

The woman stared at me in disbelieving terror. Instead of allying her fears, I had merely contrived to convince her that I was insane.

"Shall I call for help?" she asked.

Smiling at her foolishness, I began to gently remove my wrist from the dog's mouth. But the Lab had other ideas. Instead of letting me go, he clamped down harder. Not hard enough to hurt me, but hard enough to keep my wrist locked firmly inside his large dripping jaws.

"Okay, I'll take my arm back now," I told the Lab lightheartedly.

No response.

"Come on, boy, drop it," I urged the dog.

Nada.

After several fruitless minutes of gentle tugging and coaxing, I began to feel the first faint stirrings of doubt.

"Are you all right?" a man's voice asked.

Craning my neck awkwardly upward, I found myself looking into the eyes of a worried policeman.

"Yes, I'm fine," I told the anxious looking officer.

"Is this your dog?" he asked.

"No, but..."

"He seems to be biting your arm," he pointed out.

"No, actually he's just kind of holding it," I said with acute embarrassment. "He probably thinks it's a stick."

"But he won't let go?"

"No," I admitted, "not at the moment."

"Where's the owner?"

"Good question."

"In the bank," a new voice said. "I think I saw a woman going into the bank."

The voice belonged to a shoeshine man who, along with several of his brethren, had left their chairs to inspect the action. While the shoeshine man entered the bank to look for the Lab's owner, the policeman nervously urged me to remain calm.

"I am calm," I assured him.

"That dog looks mean," he said, hand on holster. "We better disable him."

"He is *not* mean," I said with conviction, from my absurdly contorted bent-over position.

"But he attacked you," the policeman insisted.

"He did not attack me! It was my fault. I…uh…stuck my wrist in his mouth."

"Why did you do that?" the policeman asked.

"Another good question," I said, as I died slowly of embarrassment. "Look. Just don't hurt the dog, okay? He's a good boy."

"*A good boy*?" The policeman could not have been more confused.

"Yes," I said, sitting down on the ground (my knees were getting sore from squatting) and petting the dog's head with my free hand. "Good boy," I crooned. "Good boy."

The shoeshine man returned a moment later with the bank manager and several stray employees, all of them shaking their heads in wonder. These, together with the three other shoeshine men, a newspaper vendor and the original elderly lady were creating quite the crowd.

"He stuck his arm in the dog's mouth!" someone said.

"What an idiot!" someone else replied.

"We're going to have to put down the dog," the policeman announced. "I'm calling for backup."

"You are *not* hurting this dog!" I declared, throwing my free arm protectively around the Lab's neck.

"Then what do we do?" the policeman demanded. "We can't leave you like this. You're creating a disturbance."

"Get a duck," I said.

"A duck? Why a duck?"

"This dog is a retriever," I explained. "It's in his blood. Show him a duck and he's sure to release my arm."

"That makes sense," the policeman said. "But where do we get the duck?"

"I know where you can get a duck," one of the shoeshine men said helpfully.

Ten minutes later a second policeman arrived on the scene, holding a deceased duck by its featherless white neck.

"No, no," I groaned, "that's a *dead* duck!"

"I know it's dead," the policeman said. "I was raised on a farm."

Then he laid the dead featherless fowl at the Lab's feet. The dog sniffed disinterestedly at the remains for a moment, before clamping down a little tighter on my wrist.

"He doesn't like the duck," the policeman said accusatorily.

"So now what do we do?" the bank manger demanded.

"Try a cheeseburger," the shoeshine man suggested.

And we did, and lo and behold, upon grabbing a whiff of the burger, the Lab released me instantly, gobbling up the entire quarter-pounder in .5 seconds. Then, furiously wagging his tail, he sat down, offered his paw, "spoke", rolled over and played dead, all in rapid succession.

"Well, all's well that end's well," I said, heading back to the bank.

"Not so fast," a man in a chef's hat said, stepping into my path. "You owe me four thousand pesos for the duck."

"*Four thousand pesos*?" I cried. "That's outrageous!"

"It comes with rice," he explained.

Plan B

Does anyone out there have any idea what a "Russian Massage" is? According to *Vallarta Vixens Today*, it involves repeated applications of warm borscht to portions of the human anatomy best left unspecified. But that seems, even to me, a tad farfetched. The reason I am asking has to do with an informal poll I took recently of husbands visiting my wife's shop.

Husbands, as all shopkeepers will tell you, are the bane of their existence. These grumpy, impatient parsimonious party-poopers despise the very notion of shopping, especially when it entails spending money on something that does not make noise, cut things in half or spew exhaust.

As I sit day after day *doing time* in Lucy's store, I have been forced to bear witness to the following grisly little drama a thousand times:

A couple walks in. The wife commences to circulate excitedly, looking at this, picking up that, while the husband stands near the door, shifting from one foot to the other, making sour faces and generally looking like someone who badly needs to make number two.

The Wife: "Honey, look at these beautiful Talavera plates; wouldn't they be wonderful in the dining room?"

The Husband: (Grunt.)

The Wife: "Which color do you like, the blue or the green?"

The Husband: (   )

The Wife: "It's only thirty dollars. Should we buy it?"

The Husband: "There's nowhere to put it."

The Wife: "Yes there is—over the credenza."

The Husband: (   ) .

The Wife: "What about this lovely hand-woven wool cushion-cover? Wouldn't it look great in the den?"

The Husband: "No room."

The Wife: "What do you mean? We already have a cushion there; this would just slip over it."

The Husband: "We're missing happy hour."

So there you have it. Husbands will not allow their wives to shop in peace. Husbands loathe shopping and would rather do almost anything else. Which brings us to the subject of my informal poll: "Speaking as a husband, what would you rather do, instead of going shopping with your wife?"

The number one answer was, of course, "Have a Russian Massage".

Other activities husbands preferred to shopping with their wives included: having a beer, receiving head, watching television, moving their bowels, reading the paper, and/or doing all of the above simultaneously.

In an attempt to pacify these impatient uncooperative individuals, I installed, inside the bathroom, a television tuned in perpetuity to *ESPN*, as well as a small newspaper stand manned by our maid's husband, Pablo. Poor Pablo, a wee waif of a fellow who fit nicely inside the shower stall, had suffered a minor mishap while driving his bus under the influence of alcohol and was temporarily unemployed.

"It wasn't my fault," he shouted to me from the bathroom. "That taco stand rolled right out in front of me. I never had a chance."

I had also intended to install inside the cozy bathroom a Russian masseuse, but it was already getting kind of cramped in there and my wife (whose creativity, refined taste and boundless energy have made of her shop, *Lucy's Cucu Cabaña*, the outstanding success it is today) nixed that plan before I could properly conduct a single job interview.

When my bathroom-cum-entertainment center failed to achieve the desired results, I came up with an inspired concept to which I affixed the acronym, *SSTFM: Shopping Sensitivity Training For Men*. Scheduling the first seminar for St. Valentine's Day, I put up posters all over town, then sat back and waited for what I hoped would be an overwhelming response.

To my bottomless disappointment, by the time the first seminar was scheduled to begin, I had acquired an audience of exactly two men.

"The idea of this seminar," I told my pair of attendees, "is to make the experience of shopping with your wives, not just bearable, but actually enjoyable. The principle technique involved is 'Visualization'. And so, I would like all of you to close your eyes and attempt to paint upon your interior canvas the following picture."

My audience dutifully closed all four of its eyes.

"All right," I continued, "now I know that most of you, when you enter a shop, do so reluctantly, and are usually trailing behind your wives, like unwilling farm animals being led to the slaughter. So I want you to visually transform the person you are feebly following. It is no longer your wife. It is instead a three-hundred-pound offensive lineman, and you are no longer an old tired husband. You are now a young, virile fleet-footed running back following your massive blocker downfield. The museum quality (but reasonably priced) wooden masks hanging on the walls are really fans cheering you on from the stands. The tables, piled high with fabulous hand-woven textiles, are actually linebackers, who you easily dodge on your way downfield for the big score!"

"Um, excuse me," one of the men said, raising his hand, but keeping his eyes shut.

"Yes?"

"What if we don't like sports?"

"You don't like sports?" I asked, aghast.

"No."

"Neither do I," the other man said.

"That's not a problem," I said, recovering quickly. "We will revert to *Visualization Number Two*. As you follow your wife into the shop, she is no longer your wife. She is now a gorgeous twenty-five-year-old blond Russian tennis player with long legs, unbelievable breasts and an impeccably firm bubble-shaped behind. And this is no Mexican gift shop you are entering. It is, in fact, a massage parlor filled with wall-to-wall mirrors, enabling you to eyeball, from every conceivable angle, all of the tantalizing cracks and crevices which are about to be revealed to you in..."

"Excuse me," one of the men said, raising his hand again.

"Yes?"

"What if we aren't interested in women?"

"What do you mean?"

"We're gay," the other man said.

"Both of you?"

"Yes."

"But then," I began, "what's the..."

"He likes to shop, but I don't," the first man told me. "We fight about it all the time. That's why we're here."

"Oh. Well, in that case, let's go directly to *Visualization Number Three*: The person you are following into the shop is *definitely* not your wife. He is, in fact, the Governor of California, buffed to the max and hung like a Christmas tree!"

Divine Altercation

As I lay on the ground, stunned and in considerable pain, the *Padré* bolted from his car and rushed to my side, already proclaiming to the world at large that he was not to blame.

"Do you speak English?" he asked in that language. In no condition to expound at any length upon my bilinguicity, I nodded my head.

"Are you badly injured?" he asked. When I did not reply, his face took on a troubled look and he mumbled something about taking me to a doctor. Seeing a doctor sounded like an excellent idea, so I nodded my head again. The *Padré*, with the help of several good Samaritans, stuffed me into the back of his car and off we went.

By the time we reached our destination my head had cleared considerably, and though I was still suffering a fair amount of pain, I did not believe that I was seriously injured. Nonetheless, having my physical integrity verified by a qualified physician was still, I decided, the prudent thing to do. And so, leaning heavily on the divinely ordained shoulder of the world's worst driver, I allowed myself to be led through a door and into what appeared to be, according to a painted sign on the wall, the office of a Gynecologist.

Watching the *Padré* half-carrying a battered gringo into her vestibule, the receptionist's face took on an expression of total panic. Even though I could not have looked all that bad, being accompanied by a priest must have made of me, in her mascara-shadowed eyes, a potentially critical case—a cadaver-in-waiting, as it were.

In any case, she ushered us at once into the doctor's inner sanctum, where I was laid to rest on a stirrupped stainless steel examination table. There then ensued an appalling conversation between the doctor and the *Padré*. Speaking in rapid Spanish, which they assumed I could not understand, the two men first reviewed the details of the accident, and then the potential problems that I could cause for the *Padré* if I was so inclined. Finally, they agreed upon a strategy for convincing me that *I* was the one at fault, and that *I* was the one who could suffer serious consequences as a result of my "reckless behavior" (walking on a sidewalk). Never once in the course of this disgraceful discussion did they even touch upon my potential injuries.

"This," the *Padré* told me in his gimpy but decipherable English, "is my brother-in-law. He is a highly qualified physician and he is going to examine you."

Though inside I was simmering with rage, I attempted to maintain a neutral expression as the Gynecologist pulled up my shirt and slid down my pants. The area around my left hip, which had taken the brunt of the impact, was badly bruised and swollen. The doctor wiped off a bit of blood, moved my leg this way and that, taped a piece of gauze over the insulted spot and said in Spanish to the *Padré*, "Tell him I said he is fine. Tell him he is perfectly fit."

"The doctor says you are fine," the *Padré* told me. "He says you have a bad bruise, but nothing is broken," he added, improvising a little. "He says you are perfectly fit."

"Really?" I said innocently. "So does that mean I can still bear children?"

"You speak Spanish!" the *Padré* and his brother-in-law intoned in simultaneous awe, as if they had just witnessed a miracle, as if I had, before their very eyes, transformed an ordinary bucket of water into a tub of contraceptive jelly.

"Yes," I replied with feigned politeness, "even if I am, as the doctor so prettily put it, 'a stupid American.'"

"I never said that," the doctor lied indignantly.

"I want to see an army-trained orthopedic specialist," I declared.

(Many of the best orthopedists and traumatologists in Mexico are army doctors who, after fulfilling their military obligations, enter private practice.)

The two men were stunned once again: How could a seemingly run-of-the-mill gringo like myself be so well versed in the intricacies of Mexican medicine?

"You're not a tourist?" the doctor asked in a quavering voice.

"I am about the furthest thing from a tourist you've ever seen," I said menacingly.

What I'd really wanted to say was that I was their worst nightmare, but the doctor looked like a *Rambo* fan, and might have heard that line before.

"Your Spanish is very good," the doctor said in a pathetically transparent attempt at softening me up with flattery. "Where did you learn it?"

"CIA," I said with a straight face.

"You're in the *CIA*?" the doctor said, all but choking on those three dreaded letters.

"Not any more. Now I work for a government agency so secret only a handful of men even know it exists. And most of them are dead. Let's get going."

"Going where?" the *Padré* asked.

"To the army doctor."

"But, but, who will pay?" the *Padré* asked.

"You, of course."

"But those doctors are very expensive," the *Padré* sniveled, "and I am only a poor priest. I'm sure you know that we take vows of poverty."

"In that case your brother-in-law can pay. He's a rich doctor, not a poor priest. I want an MRI (the most expensive procedure I could come up with in my weakened condition) and I want it now!"

"An *MRI*?" the Gynecologist grunted, as if he'd suddenly been seized with a prenatal contraction. "In my professional opinion, resorting to such an elaborate procedure at this juncture is entirely unnecessary."

"You mean," I asked evilly, "just from feeling my hip you can tell if it's a boy or a girl?"

"Well, I, uh…"

"Are you a Catholic, my son?" the *Padré* suddenly asked, apropos of nothing.

"Not even close, *Padré*," I replied smugly.

"But surely," he said, "you *believe*."

"I'll tell you what I believe, *Padré*; I believe you should go down to the *Transito* office and turn in your driver's license."

"What on earth for?"

"Let's call it an act of penance. You do have a valid driver's license?"

"Well, I'm sure I, uh, have something of that nature, though…"

"Then let's see it," I said, holding out my hand.

"I…I don't believe it is exactly what they call current," he muttered.

"Well, there's an infraction right there," I pointed out. Despite the pain in my hip I was beginning to enjoy myself. "Let's see. We've got speeding out of a House of Worship. Mowing down a pedestrian. Driving without a license. Negligence…"

"We are not conceding that the accident was entirely the *Padré*'s fault," his brother-in-law said. "After all, the pedestrian has certain obligations, too—looking where he is going, for example."

"You mean," I rejoined energetically, "when a pedestrian is walking on a *sidewalk* he is supposed to be alert for vehicles racing out into the street from church courtyards?"

"I was not speeding," the *Padré* protested. "Let's be reasonable. It was, after all, an accident, an…an…"

"An Act of God?" I suggested.

"Well, in a manner of speaking," the *Padré* said thoughtfully, "in the sense that all occurrences are, at their most profound levels, expressions of the Creator's Grand Design."

"Don't you believe in Free Will?" I asked accusatorily. "What are you, a closet Calvinist or something?"

"Of course I believe in Free Will," the priest said. "Every human being is given choices: to sin, or not to sin, to repent, or not to repent, to…"

"To be born with polio, or not to be born with polio?" I cut in. "To die of childhood meningitis, or not to die of childhood meningitis?"

"That is a separate issue," the priest said. "There are… mysteries…" he trailed off reverentially.

"Mysteries!" I snorted. "Here's a mystery, *Padré*: Where in hell did you learn to drive?"

"I was taught by my uncle," the *Padré* began, "who drove professionally for a moving…"

"Okay. Enough beating around the burning bush. It's time to go see the Orthopedist. And he better be good. I'll know if he's not. It's part of my training."

"Perhaps we should wait," the doctor suggested. "There are still several procedures I could perform without the aid of…"

"Forget it," I said, sliding painfully off the table. "Nobody's Pap-smearing this gringo—especially you!"

Naturally, on our way over to see the specialist the nervous priest ran a red light, removing, several seconds later, the rear bumper of a Volkswagen Bug which had been innocently traversing the intersection. The driver of the Bug, an attractive young woman, informed us that we were in big trouble, that her father was none other than the Chief of Police! The *Padré* and the doctor, I could see, did not receive this news gladly.

"Do you have a cell phone?" I asked her.

"Of course," she said, whipping one out of her purse.

"I think you should call your father," I said. "You won't believe me if I tell you where we were going when the *Padré* here illegally ran the red light and smashed into the rear of your vehicle."

"Where were you going?" she asked.

"These two gentlemen," I explained, "were taking me to an Orthopedic Surgeon because, just a short while ago, the *Padré*, driving this very same vehicle, ran me over in front of La Iglesia de San Juan."

"That's terrible," she said, glancing with disapproval at the two men who, judging from their malign expressions, would have liked to run me over one more time, for good measure. Carmen—that was her name—dutifully called her father, who ordered everyone to stay put and await his imminent arrival.

While we waited for the Chief, Carmen and I chatted about this and that as, concurrently, the *Padré* and his brother-in-law continued to shoot me the occasional homicidal glare.

The Chief arrived in the passenger seat of an immense tow truck, scowling and looking like he hadn't moved his bowels in a fortnight. After ascertaining that his daughter was all right, he made a rapid inspection of the accident site and then ordered both of the vehicles impounded, which was a bit unusual since, in the case of the Volkswagen, he was impounding his own car.

The *Padré* approached the Chief and began to plead his case.

"You again," the Chief interrupted him. "I should have known. I'd confiscate your license in a minute, *Padré*...if only you had one."

"Please, let me explain," the *Padré* pleaded. "We were rushing this unfortunate foreigner to a doctor—we still have to rush him to the doctor, so impounding my automobile would not be practical at this time—and what with our anxiety about his..."

"Is that true?" the Chief asked, turning to me.

"Partially, sir," I said respectfully.

"What do you mean?" the Chief demanded.

"I *was* being driven—rather erratically, I might add—to a doctor," I said, "because the *Padré* had just run me over in front of La Iglesia de San Juan."

"That is not a fair characterization," the *Padré* piped in protest. "I bumped him, that was all."

"Bumped?" I repeated with dismay. "Chief, would you like to see some of the injuries I sustained?"

"Yes, I would," he said, glaring at the *Padré*.

As I slid my pants down the several inches necessary to expose the offended joint, all eyes were upon me, especially those of the Chief's attractive daughter. I gave her my best smile and she smiled back.

"That looks like it was caused by more than just a bump," the Chief said judiciously.

"It does look serious," Carmen agreed. "I'm studying to be a nurse," she added for my benefit.

"How commendable," I remarked slyly.

The Chief, not unaware of the incipient attraction between myself and his daughter, turned to me and said, "Your Spanish is quite good. Do you live in Mexico?"

"Yes," I replied expansively, "I do indeed have the privilege of residing in this magnificent country."

"And what do you do here?"

"I am a representative of my government," I lied.

"The diplomatic corps?" he asked hopefully.

"In a manner of speaking. I'm afraid, sir, that the work I do is somewhat confidential," I said discreetly.

"I see. And you are here in *Parangaricutimicuaro* on business?"

"No, I had a week off and I thought I would take advantage of this free time to get to know some of the colonial towns."

"*Excelente!*" the Chief said. "Perhaps my daughter would like to show you some of the local sights?"

"I would be honored," I said, "if Carmen wouldn't mind putting up with my indifferent company."

"No, I would be delighted," Carmen said eagerly.

"*Excelente!*" the Chief said again. "Now, we need to get you some medical attention. We have a first-rate Orthopedist here, Dr. Macias. He has all the latest equipment. Of course the *Padré* will pay all expenses. Right, *Padré*?"

"Yes, well I suppose…"

"Does Dr. Macias happen to have an MRI machine?" I asked casually.

"Yes," Carmen answered, "his clinic is very modern."

"*Excelente!*" I said, echoing the Chief's favorite expression.

"But we agreed, no MRIs," the Gynecologist blurted out.

"I agreed to nothing," I said. "Chief, did you know that this man, who has pronounced himself fully competent to judge the extent of my injuries, is a *Gynecologist?*"

"He is? Son a raped whore!" the Chief added indelicately.

"I am still a doctor," the *Padré's* brother-in-law said, attempting to muster a few grains of dignity. "And I still say, in my expert opinion, that this man is not seriously injured and requires no further medical attention."

The Chief was outraged. "In your *expert* opinion? We are dealing with a potentially broken bone, doctor, not a frigging yeast infection! I insist upon the very best care for my so…friend, here."

I believe for a moment there the Chief had intended to say "son-in-law", but realized that he was jumping the gun a bit. Apparently, he was operating under the assumption that I was a rich gringo, which I was not. But then again, all things are relative, and by the modest standards of *Parangaricutimicuaro* perhaps I was rich and, therefore, prime son-in-law material, excepting of course the fact that I was already married.

After a period of introspection, the Chief decided to have the *Padré's* car impounded, but not his own. "You drive," he instructed his daughter. "You sit in the passenger seat," he told me. "And you two get in the back," he ordered the *Padré* and the Gynecologist.

"But why do we have to go?" the doctor protested.

"So you can pay the bill," the Chief said succinctly.

Just as we were about to pull away, the Chief leaned his head inside the window. "Call me on my cell phone," he told me, "if there's any problem." As he said the word "problem" he shot the backseat passengers an unmistakably cautionary glare.

"Sure thing," I said with filial devotion. "By the way, Chief," I whimpered with conviction, "now that the shock is wearing off, everything is starting to hurt all of a sudden. Maybe I should have a full-body scan, just to be on the safe side."

"Good idea," the Chief agreed. "*Excelente.*"

"*Infernum gringoius paininthebuttocksium,*" the *Padré* muttered morosely.

Beware of Man

One day a year I allow myself the luxury of actually saying what I think. This small bit of self-indulgence is a wonderful aid to me in several ways: it helps to relieve months of accumulated stress, and it improves dramatically the odds of being fired from my job.

This year, on what I call *My Perverse Day*, I arrived at work a few minutes early and placed a sign in the window, reading: "Beware of Me". Then I sat down behind my desk and waited for the morning influx of victims—I mean, customers.

The first clients in the door were a couple who were so different from each other they could have qualified as separate species. The husband was ill-humored and restless, a man who would rather swallow spent fuel rods than spend the morning shopping. The wife was attractive, spirited and overflowing with positive energy. Taking her time, she sashayed around the shop basking in the radiance of our superbly crafted merchandise.

Every so often the glum husband directed at his pretty wife a series of impatient grunting sounds, which might or might not have been attempts at reproducing human speech. Finally, receiving no response from her, he turned to me and said, purely out of boredom, "I bet you're an American."

"How much?" I asked.

"How much? No, no, I didn't want to—That was just a figure of speech. I meant, judging by your accent, you must be an American."

"I have been assiduously practicing my English language skills," I replied in my best Hindustani accent, "for the past fifty-five years."

"So," the husband said irritably, "you *are* an American?"

"First and foremost," I replied pedantically, "I consider myself a human being. These silly distinctions we make (nationality, race, religion) are so superficial and meaningless. Do you realize that the DNA of your average bark beetle only varies from that of a homo sapiens by one percent? Isn't that unbelievable! Doesn't that mean, as humans, we are all so fundamentally alike that to dwell upon our differences is pointless, counterproductive and spiritually deflating?"

"Nancy," the man said to his wife, "I'll wait for you outside."

"Gee," I said after he'd left, "I think I might have offended your husband."

"Don't worry about it," Nancy said kindly. "He's always offended by something. He has absolutely no sense of humor. I thought what you said made perfect sense. And I love that Indian accent," she added with an ironic smile.

"Thanks," I said. "I hope you don't mind me saying this, Nancy, but you are a very attractive woman. And though we have only known each other a short time, I would venture to guess that you are quite intelligent, as well. So, if I may be so blunt, what are you doing with a *Rent a Wreck* like him?"

"Good question," Nancy said, looking me boldly in the eye. "Are you married?"

"Yes I am, Nancy. Happily so, unfortunately. Otherwise I'd offer to close the shop right now and waltz you across the road to the *Hotel Jalisco*."

"What would you do about my husband?" she giggled.

"Have him arrested, I suppose. For loitering or..."

At that moment a nervous-looking couple walked in the door and asked in desperate tones where they could find the bus to Mismaloya.

"Right across the street," I said politely.

"The one parked over there?" the wife asked.

"Ma'am," I replied patiently, "it is the only bus visible from the interior of this shop. Which is owned by my wife," I added with supreme irrelevance, "who refuses to fire me."

"So that's it, right across the street?" her husband asked.

"Yes, sir," I said, a wee note of sarcasm coloring my voice, "that long green thing with all the chairs in it."

Nancy began to giggle.

"You don't have to use that tone of voice," the man said unpleasantly. "We were just asking a question."

"By my count, sir, you asked three questions, two of them entirely unnecessary. If, however, you wish to lodge a complaint with the owner I will be happy to provide you with her cell number. Our *Customer Complaint* lines are open twenty-four hours a day. In fact, we prefer you to call between the hours of two and four am, so that our overworked operators can attend to your needless nit-picking on a more timely basis."

"So it's that bus right there?" the wife said, pointing out the window.

"Jesus, Mary and Joseph!" I moaned. "Are we deaf, dumb and blind? Are we from Outer Space? Are we *Registered Republicans*? Tell me, God, where did I go wrong!"

As he was ushering his wife out the door, the inflamed husband turned around and said, "If you ask me, you need professional help."

"You're right about that," I told his fleeing back. "If you happen to meet any proctologists around the pool, please, send them my way."

The Mismaloya bus seekers were replaced within moments by Nancy's husband, followed by a nice-looking couple from North Dakota.

As Nancy's husband tried unsuccessfully to drag Nancy out the door, the North Dakota wife began to ogle our miniature section. The North Dakota husband, meanwhile, who had about as much interest in shopping as I did in contracting the bubonic plague, approached my desk in a doomed attempt at making idle conversation.

"So, you live here?" he asked—one of my all-time favorite questions.

"No, I just work here," I replied. "I live in a house."

Standing by the Oaxacan painted animal display, Nancy began to giggle again.

"Oh," North Dakota said. "Have you lived in Mexico long?"

"Twenty-two years."

"That's a long time. Do you like it?"

"Like what?"

"Living in Mexico."

"Not really," I said. "If they'd only drop the charges, I'd go back to my old life in Detroit in a Michigan minute."

"Charges?" the man said, furrowing his brow. "What did you do in Detroit?"

"Robbed banks, mostly," I said matter-of-factly. "May I ask you a question?"

"I suppose so."

"Could you loan me five hundred dollars?"

Looking hugely embarrassed, he replied, "So, in twenty-two years you must have seen a lot of changes around here?"

"Yes."

After a long and uncomfortable pause, he said, "Well, what do you think has changed the most?"

"Me," I said. "I have a lot less hair on my head now, but more of it on my back."

"The town," Mr. North Dakota foolishly persisted, "what has changed about the *town* since you've lived here?"

"Oh, the town," I said expansively, "I could talk all day about the town: the ambiance, the atmosphere, the environment. The streets, the roads, the avenues—the total municipal manifestation, as it were. I mean, get real, amigo!"

"It's gotten bigger then?" he asked, eyeing the exit.

"Listen," I told him, "when I first got here there were no traffic lights."

"Really?"

"No cable TV, no appliance stores, no imported goods of any kind. No street lights, no public toilets, no extension cords," I ranted on with mounting hysteria. "No running water, no walls, no windows, no law and order. It was a jungle, mister, overrun by rapacious reptiles, flesh-eating plants and salacious salesmen! There were alligators the length of tractor trailers swiveling their snouts up and down the Malecon! There were mosquitoes the size of Guyanese grapefruits draining the lifeblood of the community. There were…"

"Honey," the man told his wife, "I'll wait for you outside."

Time's Up

Nacho was broke yet again, and in need of what he called (in a tsunami of understatement) a "small favor". He had a friend, he informed me, in federal prison, who was desperately depressed, on the very verge of committing suicide.

"That's too bad, Nacho," I said sympathetically. "From what I understand, being in federal prison isn't all it's cracked up to be."

"*Cracked up to be*?" Nacho's grasp of idiomatic English was impressive, but not infinite. "What does that mean?"

"Nothing, Nacho, I was just making a little joke."

"A joke? I do not understand. This is not funny. It is a batter of life and death. I must go to my friend at once."

"It's a *matter*," I corrected my friend.

"What's a matter?" Nacho demanded nervously.

"No, Nacho, it's what's *the* matter."

"Yes, that is what I want to know," Nacho asked urgently, "what is the matter?"

"Nothing is the matter," I said reassuringly.

"Is that definite?"

"Quite."

"Then you will help me?"

"Help you do what?"

"I need a ride. To see my friend. Before he hangs himself. Or splits his wrists!"

"A *ride*? Nacho, that's a five-hour drive—each way. And it's *slits*, not *splits*."

"Yes," Nacho said, suddenly brimming with optimism, "if we depart at first light, we will be home in time for dinner."

From the back of my throat there escaped a long drawn-out groan, to which Nacho replied, "Great! Fantastic! We leave at day-brick?"

By noon the next day Nacho and I we were standing outside the main gate of the *Salinas de Gortari Federal Institute for Social Rehabilitation and Public Security* on the outskirts of Guadalajara.

The *SGFISRPS*, as it was known for short, could not have been more hideous, with its bare cinderblock walls, rust-stained guard towers and (the icing on the cake) enough sagging razor wire to slice and dice a whole sub-continent of would-be escapees.

In response to Nacho's gentle prodding of a peeling button, a uniformed individual with a spectacularly large stomach approached the gate and asked us what we wanted. Nacho told him, in a hundred words or less, what our intentions were. By way of reply, the man emitted an odd grunting-burping sound. Then, after attempting in vain to hitch his pants up over his mountainous midriff, he led us across a dusty courtyard, opened a door and dumped us inside a small dark office where a full-figured female official stood behind a scarred and dented gunmetal-gray counter, eyeing us with distaste.

"*Buenas tardes*," Nacho said with a smile.

"*Buenas tardes*," she replied venomously.

Once again, with elaborate courtesy, Nacho stated his business.

"Who's the visitor?" she asked gruffly, "you or him?"

"I am," Nacho said. "He just came along for the ride."

"Well," she announced with a self-satisfied smirk, "he can go in, but you can't."

"What do you mean?" Nacho asked in dismay. "I told you, I am the visitor. He is just my driver. What is the problem?"

"Your clothes are the problem," the woman explained. "They're the same color as the inmates' uniforms. We have strict rules here. No exceptions."

"But I have come all the way from Puerto Vallarta," Nacho declared.

"Congratulations," she said, massively unimpressed.

Maintaining a calm demeanor, Nacho pled his case skillfully and at great length, but he might as well have been imploring the proverbial stone wall (which the prison matron did in fact resemble) for all the good it did.

"Why don't you two exchange clothes," the woman said with an evil grin. "You could use the bathroom over at the gas station."

"Very funny," I muttered. The top of Nacho's head was flush with the bottom of my chin, but even so he outweighed me by more than ninety pounds.

Nacho said, "You will have to go in my place."

"Forget it," I said emphatically. "I don't even know the man."

"You must see him," Nacho said. "He is desperate for company. You could be saving his life."

"What about his fellow inmates? What's wrong with their company?"

"They are common criminals," Nacho said disdainfully.

"And your friend isn't? What did this guy *do* anyway?"

"A misunderstanding," Nacho mumbled.

"How do you commit a misunderstanding, Nacho?"

"It was an accident."

"What was an accident?"

"Under normal circumstances, he would never hurt a flea."

"He hurt someone?"

"Ramon is a wonderful person," Nacho said loyally. "The knife belonged to his cousin. He…"

"So this Ramon person stabbed someone? Is that why he's in prison?"

"So, you will see him?" Nacho asked. "Good," he said, before I could frame a reply. "He will go in my place," he informed the corpulent woman, who immediately handed me a dozen forms to sign.

"Now empty your pockets," she commanded me once I had signed the stack of papers. Dutifully, I laid my belongings (my keys, my wallet, some loose change) on the scarred metal counter.

"Now take off your hat," she said.

I handed her my hat.

"And your belt," she added.

"I'd rather keep my belt on, if you don't mind," I said. "I'm just a few months out of surgery and everything is kind of loose on me still, so…"

"Take off your belt!"

Beltless, hatless, keyless and walletless, I was ushered into a closet-sized room at the rear of the office. "Nacho, what the hell should I tell your friend?" I called back over my shoulder.

"Just tell him you came in my place," Nacho said, "and try to convince him that life is worth living. Maybe you could…"

The massive iron door was slammed shut in Nacho's face, cutting his last suggestion off at the nose.

Inside the small airless chamber I was gently frisked by a hefty male guard and allowed to pass into another room. With a foreboding clang, a second door was closed and locked behind me. Fighting the urge to scream, "But I'm innocent!" I shuffled reluctantly up to yet another battered metal counter.

From behind the counter a badly overweight man (the collective carbohydrate consumption of the *SGFISRPS* staff must have been formidable) handed me a small metal disk with some numbers etched into it. "Whatever you do," he said sternly, "don't give this to anyone. Without it, you won't be allowed to leave the prison."

Fighting off a Category Five panic attack, I laughed nervously and said, "You're joking."

"This is a maximum security prison," the guard said, stuffing his mouth with a handful of chile-flavored potato chips. "We don't joke."

Perhaps, I thought, as the guard glared at me, obesity is a job requirement here. Given their ample abdomens, the *SGFISRPS* personnel would never have to go around, like I was, with their hands clutching the loose waists of their trousers. And having both of their appendages fully available could be of great value in the event of a prison break, or a food fight.

With my right hand, the one not holding my pants up, I formed a fist around the all-important metal disk and thrust the whole enchilada deep inside my pocket, hoping that no one would mistake it for a concealed weapon. Then I followed the guard through a series of metal gates and doors (all of which were locked behind us), deeper and deeper into the bleak heart of the *Salinas de Gortari Federal Institute for Social Rehabilitation and Public Safety*.

At yet another rusting metal counter, manned by a former female shot-put champion, I was asked to present the disk.

Reluctantly, I opened my fist and displayed the chunk of metal.

"Please give it to me," she said, holding out her hand.

Certain that this was some type of test, I said, "No way. I give this disk to no one."

"They meant, don't give it to an inmate, *Señor*," she said patronizingly. "They weren't talking about staff. I need to write down the numbers."

"Fine. I'll read them to you."

Without warning the extensively bicepped woman reached out and grabbed my hand. A short struggle ensued which I, outnumbered two hands to one, quickly lost.

This is one strong matron, I thought, as I prepared to go provisionally bottomless, if that's what it was going to take to regain sole possession of my precious disk. After recording the numbers in a ledger, however, she simply handed it back to me. "Whatever you do, *Señor*," she ordered me in her gravelly voice, "don't give that disk to anyone!"

Another guard appeared, a man so fat it would have taken a modern-day Magellan to circumnavigate his waist.

"Do you have your disk?" he demanded ominously.

Squeezing the metal token hard enough to draw blood, I nodded my head.

"Good. Then follow me," he said, "and don't get lost."

Given the directness of our route (down a single hallway) and the size of my guide (it would have been easier to mislay the floor), getting lost was not a major worry. Indeed, my only concern at that particular moment was how to remove my skinny white ass (intact) from the grim confines of the *SGFISRPS* as quickly as possible.

Two more iron doors were opened, then shut and locked behind us, their noisy metal mechanisms sounding to my increasingly apprehensive ears like the ominous clanging clacking bells of Doom Incarnate.

Then we passed into an especially long lime-green hallway, at the end of which was the *final door*. Before locking me in behind it, the globular guard said, "You've got one hour."

"I don't need an hour!" I wanted to shout. But instead of shouting I turned around, and there was Ramon, a small wiry fellow with a face like a ferret. Ramon, as promised, looked utterly miserable, but more than that, he looked surprised.

"Who the fuck are you?" he demanded.

"I'm a friend of Nacho's," I said nervously. "They wouldn't let him in because he was wearing the wrong clothes. And we're kind of different sizes, so we couldn't, uh...So, he sent me in his place."

"He sent *you* in his place?" Ramon asked with disbelief.

"Well, yes," I said without enthusiasm.

Needless to say, every facet of my current situation was conspiring to make me feel increasingly ill-at-ease: being locked up deep inside a Mexican prison; my beltless pants, which were just an opened fist away from falling to the floor; the fear of losing my metallic pass to freedom; and last but not least, being confined alone in this windowless room with a morbidly depressed convicted *whatever*—a man I was somehow expected to talk out of committing suicide!

"So now what?" Ramon asked.

"I'm supposed to, you know, try to make you feel better," I said lamely.

Ramon digested this for a moment and then cast an eye at the room's only furnishing, a small cot built into the wall. "Okay," he said, a strange predatory look clouding his dark eyes, "let's get started." So saying, he began to unfasten his pants.

"Wait a minute!" I shouted. "What is this?"

"A conjugal visit," Ramon replied, undoing his fly. "What did you think it was?"

Oh my God!

Clutching my loose pants with renewed vigor, I yanked them halfway up to my chin. Then, grinning like the unnerved nitwit I was, I began to hyperventilate.

"Whoa, Ramon!" I gasped. "This is not on the program."

"What do you mean?" he asked, taking a step forward.

"Well," I said, taking a step back, "I thought we were just going to have a nice little chat about the power of positive thinking. You-you-you know, Ramon," I stuttered philosophically, "every cloud has a silver lining, and…"

"I don't feel like talking," Ramon said, striding purposefully in my direction, "I feel like…"

"Yes, well, of course, Ramon, I know exactly how you feel. I mean, who wouldn't feel that way, being locked up in here like a… like a criminal, for Christ's sake. But, um, Ramon, please try to remember: It's always darkest before the dawn. And birds…uh…birds in the bush are worthless. You might as well forget about them entirely. Whereas birds in the hand are…um…uh…."

"What the hell are you talking about?" Ramon snarled.

"I'm talking, Ramon, about the fact that, uh…time's up! GUARD!" I screamed, "GET ME OUT OF HERE!"

Lady Macroach

O nly days after the *Red Tide* had slithered away like a bloody oil slick from our indignant shores, Gertie burst into my bedroom, unannounced and uninvited, in order to inform me that the "second plague" had already struck, and its name was, "Cockroaches!"

"It's an invasion!" she decreed hoarsely. "Just like in the Bible."

"Weren't those locusts, Gertie?" I asked reasonably.

"Locusts, roaches, crickets—what's the difference?"

Certain that such subtle entomological distinctions would be lost on my batty neighbor, I pled indigestion and went to go barricade myself inside the bathroom—the only place I knew for a fact where Gertie would not follow me.

That same night, stumbling into the kitchen at three am to retrieve a glass of juice, I was confronted by a sight so singularly hideous it almost made me want to move to Manitoba: an entire rugby team of giant roaches *scrumming* around the lower circumference of an upended papaya! Paralyzed with astonishment I stood staring helplessly as the thumb-sized bandits scattered helter-skelter with the blinding speed characteristic of their species.

In the days that followed I continued to encounter indecent numbers of these unwholesome creatures, and in the most unwelcome places: inside my shoes, inside my shorts, inside a half-filled pot of freshly brewed coffee and once, worst of all, perched atop my *Sonicare* toothbrush.

Having lived for so many years in an old and porous beach house, I had long-since grown accustomed to the infrequent roach, the odd ant, the occasional crab and the sporadic gecko scooting, scuttling and sneaking around my home. But this—this wholesale incursion—was more than I was prepared to bear.

"You were right," I told Gertie, who sat on my terrace gulping coffee and suavely smoking an odd-looking cigarette through a tarnished ivory holder.

"Of course I was right," she exhaled theatrically. "Have you fumigated?"

"Not yet."

"What are you waiting for?" she demanded. "Can't you see it's war! No quarter asked, none given. Take no prisoners. Either you're with them, or you're against us!"

It had been ten years since Lucy and I had last fumigated our home, and I was loathe to do it even now. My reasons were various. As a practicing non-denominational Buddhist, I believed firmly in the *Sanctity of All Life*. I did not like the idea of poison, either. But above all, my wife had a great fondness for the hundred or so non-combatant geckos who cohabitated our home, most of whom would be annihilated in a full-scale fumigation.

"Well, Lucy…" I began weakly.

"Don't go away," Gertie said, uncoiling herself like a rusty spring from the *equipale* chair, "I'll be right back."

True to her word Gertie returned in short order sporting, in addition to her pink and powder blue housecoat, elbow-length rubber gloves, a surgical mask and a pair of goggles. In her right rubbered-hand she held the largest can of *Raid* I had ever seen. "*Cosco*," she explained. "Let's get started."

Reluctantly I explained to Gertie my inconformity with the massacre of so many innocent geckos.

"Collateral damage," she replied briskly, "unavoidable in wartime. Besides, those filthy little lizards are just as bad as the roaches. A health hazard. Ever have one drop its goop on you when you're lying in bed? It happened to Bernie once. He was sleeping on his back with his mouth wide open, snoring like a water buffalo. Had to call in the paramedics."

After a lengthy debate which touched upon, among other things, respecting the "wishes of my wife", the "Oneness of Nature" and the "bacteria count per cubic millimeter of roach droppings", Gertie sighed with disgust and said, "Well, there is another way."

"What's that, Gertie—tactical nukes?"

"No, boric acid," she said, withdrawing from her purse a plastic bag of white crystalline powder.

"That looks like cocaine, Gertie."

"Don't be smart."

"But boric acid's an eye-wash. How in the world…"

"Trust me, it works. Let's get going. Those flat little filth wagons are multiplying as we speak."

Gertie marched straightaway into the kitchen where she came to stand ramrod straight, hands on hips, surveying the scene—like General Patton in drag. "So, where are they?" she demanded.

"Well, everywhere," I replied.

"Our first objective," Gertie announced, "is to locate their supply routes."

"Maybe you better lay off the *CNN* awhile," I cautioned my neighbor. "I think it's affecting your brain." Gertie favored me with an officer's scowl, as if I were a soldier who had farted himself out of formation. "All right," I said, "how do we find the supply routes?"

"We search," Gertie said with relish, "for *roachsign*."

She meant, I assumed, those small black particles of roach matter I had seen scattered about the nibbled papaya. "Here's some," I said, indicating a spot on the floor.

Gertie held out the plastic bag and ordered me to begin sprinkling, making sure I covered the edges of the floor as well as the insides of the lower kitchen cabinets. When the bag was empty I stood up and said, "I can't believe *cucarachas* will eat boric acid."

"They don't eat it, dummy; they walk on it."

"And that kills them?"

"Not right away," Gertie said, her octogenarian eyes sparkling with sadistic glee. "It takes a while. But don't worry; tomorrow morning you'll find them all over the place, lying on their backs, their little legs wriggling in the air, their disgusting antennae…"

"All right, all right, I get the picture, Gertie. What do I owe you for the ordnance?"

"Only thirty pesos," Gertie said selflessly. "I'm not charging you for my time."

Butting In

Something rather awful happened the other day at my wife's shop, where I have been working under protest for the past ten years.

A man—a *very large* man—walked in the door and, before I could say a word in protest, stuffed himself like an oversized cork into a beautifully hand-carved and painted bench, one of our most expensive items. The bench, though commodious as well as sturdy, was no match for the super-sized sitter. Above the sounds of traffic wafting in from the street, I could clearly hear the sound of wood cracking. This, I knew, was one chair we would never sell.

After the man left, I began to consider the entire situation, coming to the conclusion that this colossal dark cloud could, if I played my cards correctly, turn out to have a bright pink lining.

Always on the lookout for a way to create shopping mayhem in the hopes of finally exhausting the patience of my saintly wife, I took out my crayons and began to fashion a sign. I am no artist and it took me several tries to get it just right. Once I was satisfied with the small placard, I set it upon the crippled chair and waited to see what would happen next.

As it turned out nothing happened for quite some time. Oh, I had customers, all right, and sold, among other things, several lovely copper vases and a pair of peerless Talavera plates. But all of my clients were disgustingly slender, and none of them appeared inclined to sit down. To my bottomless disappointment, the only thing they wanted to do was *shop*!

Finally, just after six, an ocean liner of a man steamed slowly into the store and made directly for the bench.

"Excuse me, sir," I said, as he prepared to lower himself into the forbidden piece of furniture, "didn't you see the sign?"

"What sign?"

"The one on the chair," I said with a smile. "The one that reads: *'If Your Butt Don't Fit, You Must Not Sit!'*"

The man, needless to say, was not pleased. And several other clients, all women, who were browsing here and there, appeared to redden with embarrassment.

"You're telling me I cannot *sit* in this chair?" he said testily.

"I'm telling you, sir, that you do not *fit* in this chair," I replied respectfully.

"What are you talking about," he said, "that's a big chair. Of course I fit."

"Sir, it is not my function to enter into disputes with our valued clients. There is a very simple way to determine which one of us is correct."

"Of course there is," the man said, "I'll just sit down."

"No, no, no," I rushed to say. "That's not what I meant."

"Well then, what *did* you mean?" he snarled.

The women shoppers, though pretending to be immersed in *Lucy's* outstanding collection of coconut dolls, were, I could see, hanging on our every word.

"Measure," I said, withdrawing a tape measure from the drawer of my desk.

"Measure?" he shouted. "Measure what?"

"Well," I said, "the width of the chair is already known: twenty-seven inches. So then, all we have to *ascertain* is if your maximum, ah, *girth*, shall we say, exceeds that number. Simple arithmetic."

Two women standing by the plate display began to titter uncontrollably.

"This is outrageous!" the man declared. "I happen to be a repeat customer. Where's the owner. She knows me personally."

"I'm sorry," I said leaping out from behind my desk, tape measure at the ready, "Lucy's having a pedicure. But I can give you her cell, if you wish to lodge a complaint."

"Yes, I definitely want to call her."

"Fine, you can use our phone," I said agreeably. "Just let me get this measurement," I added, stretching out the tape behind his back.

"Get away from me with that thing!" he shouted, reaching for the phone. "What's the number?"

I gave him the number and he dialed.

Lucy answered the call as she was getting out of her car in front of the shop. I could see her plainly through the window.

"Is this Lucy?" the man said into the phone. "I'm John Russell, one of your biggest clients."

"You can say that again," I said in a stage whisper to the tittering women.

"That's right, John Russell. You remember me, don't you? I thought you would. I'm calling to complain about the man you have working in the shop…What has he done now? I'll tell you…Will you *please* get away from my butt!" he roared at me.

I was, at that moment, squatting directly behind him, attempting to draw a bead on his extensive *gluteus maximi*. "No, I wasn't talking to you," he said into the phone. "First he wouldn't let me sit down, and now he's trying to measure my backside…No, I'm not buying a pair of pants!"

"Sir," I said, straightening up, "I was right. It's a definite no-can-sit situation. Thirty-three and a half inches! If I'm not mistaken, that's a new *Lucy's Cucu Cabaña* record. Congratulations!" I added. "You've just won a free calendar!"

"What is going on here?" Lucy demanded, stalking into the shop and glaring at the tape dangling limply from my hand.

"We have a winner!" I informed my wife.

"Mr. Russell," she said, "I am so sorry. My husband must have forgotten to take his medication again. According to the Vet, he has a chemical imbalance in his brain and is not responsible for his actions."

"Ruff! Ruff!" I barked agreeably.

"Oh, there's no problem," Mr. Russell said cheerfully. "I can't believe I actually won something. I'll take that free calendar now, if you don't mind. Then I've got to run. I'm late for lunch."

The Siege of Edwige

Shortly after moving to Vallarta I received an unexpected visit from my cousin Lenny and his attorney, Charles.

Lenny, a successfully insane bass player in Los Angles, was also a talented mimic. His favorite targets were obnoxious New York-based celebrities (both living and dead). On previous occasions he had driven Lucy and me nearly insane with prolonged impersonations of Howard Cosell and Donald Trump.

Charles, his attorney, was thirty, tall, trim and handsome. He had (according to Charles) never lost a case, or known a woman he could not seduce, or a sport he could not master, etc., ad nauseum, and so forth.

Lucy and I took Lenny aside while Charles was out swimming laps in the ocean. Why, we demanded to know, had Lenny introduced this aggressive alpha male motor-mouth into our tranquil beach home.

"I owe him five grand," my cousin confessed.

"So?"

"So this is his payment, you know, in lieu of cash."

Lucy spoke to Lenny like a mother to a wayward child, "Lenny, what are you talking about?"

"I promised him a free week in Vallarta," Lenny explained. "Airfare, room, board and sex—all at my expense."

"What about our expense?" I asked.

"Yeah, right, that too," Lenny said. "Trust me, I cut myself a great deal: the airfare was only three hundred bucks; you're providing the accommodations; and Lucy should have no problem finding him a willing mate or two. That leaves me with a net gain of forty-seven hundred smackeroos. So where's the raicilla?"

Puerto Vallarta, in the winter of 1985, had no shortage of attractive single women. And Charles, despite his obnoxious personality, had money, good looks and that pseudo-superior swagger which some women, masochists mostly, find so attractive.

But Charles was impossibly picky. Every time Lucy would point out a possible date, the lawyer would pronounce the potential victim, "Not quite up to my standards."

After a few fruitless days, Lenny began to grow desperate. "*Lack of consummation* is a deal-buster!" he reminded me in the voice of Donald Trump.

Then, as we sat nursing beers on Los Muertos Beach, Charles spotted a beautiful young blond who made him perk up like a Pointer in a duck pond.

"Now, *that* is more like it," Charles crowed. "Do you know her?"

"She's French," Lucy, who knew everyone, replied. "Her name is Edwige. But I don't think she's a good candidate; she's super stuck-up, and I've heard she's…"

"Perfect," Charles interrupted her. "I love a good challenge. You make the date and I'll take care of the rest."

"I'll see what I can do," Lucy said, favoring the horny attorney with a dangerous smile.

Two nights later Lucy and I found ourselves seated in the old Cine Bahia, half of a hastily arranged double-date (Lenny was *hors de combat* with a massive raicilla hangover). For only the second time in its uncolorful history, our favorite movie theatre was putting on a live show: a troupe of Cuban dancers and musicians imported especially for the occasion. Edwige, it turned out, was a huge fan of Cuban music. She was also congenitally cheap, and so agreed to the date at once.

As we waited for the show to begin, Lucy and I were treated to the following thought-provoking dialogue:

"*I graduated number two in my class at Stanford Law School,*" Charles, modestly, to Edwige.

"*Very nice,*" Edwige, bored out of her pommes de terres, to Charles.

"*I'm closing in on the two-century mark, income-wise,*" Charles, leaning halfway into Edwige's chair. "*And I've been A-listed for a partnership.*"

"*Very good,*" Edwige, staring straight ahead, an L-shaped block of ice.

"Do you think Charles will hit a home run tonight?" I whispered into Lucy's ear.

"Not likely," Lucy whispered back.

"Why not? Some women really go for that type."

"Not Edwige," Lucy giggled, "she's a lesbian."

"What?"

"I tried to tell him at the beach," Lucy whispered, "but the idiot kept interrupting me."

As our prolonged and hysterical fit of laughter finally subsided, the curtain parted and the show began. The ten-piece orchestra, torrid and tight, was fronted by a frenetic middle-aged female singer, one of the most electric performers I'd ever seen. At one point, in fit of ecstasy, she tore the wig right off her head and threw it to the ground, like a football player "spiking" the ball after a touchdown. Many years later we learned that this firecracker of a woman was in fact the legendary *Queen of Salsa*, Celia Cruz.

Halfway through the second number the dancers came out, four highly attractive young men and women dressed in little linen loincloths. Period.

The previous year the Cine Bahia had made Vallarta history presenting a "play" which more resembled a live sex act. And now they'd imported nearly nude dancers all the way from Cuba. Hadn't anyone bothered to inform the management that Mexico was a conservative Catholic country where public displays of nudity were unheard of?

Apparently not…thank God.

One of the dancers, a copper-colored goddess, was so extraordinarily beautiful I couldn't tear my eyes off her; and neither, I noticed, could Edwige. Meanwhile, Charles, listing heavily date-ward, was urgently whispering God only knew what (his net worth?) into Edwige's indifferent ear.

By the sixth song the sensual dancing combined with the scorching music had turned on the entire audience, especially Edwige who, despite her tender age, appeared to be on the point of apoplexy. Charles, clueless in Vallarta, was as pleased as punch. Badly misinterpreting the source of Edwige's arousal, the young attorney sat there glowing with self-congratulatory glee, like a salesman who is about to close the biggest deal of the decade.

After the show the two women repaired to the ladies room, and I was left alone in the lobby with Lenny's lawyer.

"So, how's it going with Edwige?" I asked.

"I've got her eating right out of the palm of my hand," Charles replied smugly. "She's so hot, we'll probably skip dinner and go straight back to her condo for a little one-on-one."

"Pretty sure of yourself, aren't you, Charles?"

"I haven't met a woman yet who can resist me," he boasted shamelessly. "By midnight your deadbeat cousin will finally be off the hook for the five grand he owes me."

Uh-oh, I thought, suddenly remembering the "No Consummation" clause in Lenny's contract. Then I got an idea.

"Say, Charles," I remarked casually, "are you a betting man?"

"Only if I'm betting on a sure thing."

"How about you seducing Edwige? Would that qualify as a sure thing?"

"A more certain thing there never was," Charles declared.

"I disagree, Charles. I think she's way out of your league. In fact, I'll bet you five grand that you and Edwige *don't* get it on. What do you say?"

"That's a lot of money," Charles said. "Can you afford to lose it?"

"No *problema*," I replied. "How about you?"

"Me? Are you kidding? Didn't I tell you I've been A-listed for a..."

"Yes, several times. So, do we have a bet?"

"Your funeral," Charles said, shaking my hand.

The next morning as Lenny, Lucy and I sat on the terrace drinking coffee and watching a flock of dive-bombing pelicans decimate a hapless school of sardines, Charles showed up looking like he'd just (barely) survived a natural disaster himself.

Edwige, who it turned out was something of a sadist—at least where men were concerned—had in fact allowed Charles to spend the night with her, teasing, tormenting and torturing the A-listed lawyer all night long with impassioned promises, none of them fulfilled.

"So, uh, how'd it go, Chucky?" Lenny asked his attorney.

"I need coffee," Charles groaned. "How did what go?"

"Your hot date with Edwige," Lucy chirped, pouring him a cup. "Did you have a nice time?"

"Oh, yeah, well, that," Charles said evasively. "Let me get some caffeine in me and..."

"Come on, Charles," Lenny interrupted in the voice of Howard Cosell, "millions of sports fans all over the world are waiting with bad breath to hear, directly from your chapped lips, the genuine unvarnished uncontested truth: Did you, or did you not consummate the deal?"

"I'm trying to tell you," the bedraggled young attorney, who seemed to be missing several patches of skin on his arms and legs, said hoarsely, "if you'd just shut up for one second! The truth is, we started doing a lot of heavy rubbing just before midnight—she called it 'making *fromage*'. But she wouldn't let me kiss her, and then she wouldn't let me touch her. She just kept rubbing and rubbing. At first it felt pretty good, but then, after a while..."

"Charles!" Lenny broke in again. "Enough of this piddling and paddling about. Can you just tell us, in fifty words or less, was there or was there not internationally recognized, actual, bona fide penetration?"

"I made my best moves," Charles moaned. "I poured on the charm, hour after hour...I...Will you take a check?" he asked, turning to me.

"No need for that, Charles," I said graciously. "Just apply it to Lenny's bill. He and I'll work it out later. Right, Cuz?"

"Right, Cuz," Lenny agreed, "I'll reimburse you with the movie rights: *The Siege of Edwige*—soon to be a majuh motion pictuh!"

Band on the Rum

Every year Consuelo, my mother-in-law, comes to visit us on her birthday. And every year we give her an elaborate party featuring fireworks and live music. This year my wife and her mom had set their hearts on a funky four-piece *Norteño* band. Unfortunately, the band proved to be more elusive than the *Scarlet Pimpernel*. In just over a week it had been fired by five separate employers. Then we heard through the Mariachi-vine that the problematic musicians had finally acquired a steady gig working in a rustic cantina an hour outside of town.

"You have to go talk to them," Lucy said.

"I thought we had an agreement," I reminded her. "You organize the party; I pay for it. Division of whatever. Right?"

"Right," she said, "but this is a special case."

And she went on to explain the precise nature of this special case, which in a few words came down to this: Their *Norteño* group (the one they could not continue to exist without) was the house band for a raunchy red-light *rancho*—no place for a pair of respectable women, so…

"So," I said, unable to believe my ears, "*you* want *me* to go to a whorehouse?"

"To contract the band," my wife said.

"Not to contract anything else," my eighty-year-old *suegra* added, shooting me a meaningful look.

The *rancho* was located in the geophysical center of nowhere and not easy to find. Most of the men I asked for directions laughed or winked lewdly at me. One fellow, who might have been a wee bit soused, actually proceeded to make a number of wild gyrations with his hips and puckering movements with his mouth, before falling face-first in the dirt.

Eventually, when I did in fact locate the establishment (a study in crumbling cement), criminally loud canned music was blaring from all its windows, but the band was nowhere to be found.

The first floor looked exactly like what it was, a small rustic cantina; all of the Old Testament-type business (converting tequila into semen, and so forth) was conducted upstairs. Behind the badly battered bar there stood a plump pretty woman displaying several soccer fields of cleavage.

"*Buenas tardes,*" I said.

"*Buenas tardes,*" she smiled lasciviously back.

"I'm looking for four men who…"

"If you're looking for men, you're in the wrong place," she told me. "But, if you want four women, that's another story."

"No, no, no," I said. "I want the house band, a quartet that plays *Norteño* music."

The barmaid shook her head. "What a waste," she said sadly, "a good-looking guy like you and…"

"I want to contract the band to play at a party," I interrupted her. "At my house."

"Oh, I see. What kind of party?"

"A birthday party."

"I love a good birthday party," she said brightly. "Do you need someone to jump out of the cake? I'm available."

"I'm sure you are. But it's not that kind of party. It's for my…"

"I have lots of experience," she insisted.

"No doubt. Give me a *Corona*, please," I said, hoping she'd become more cooperative if I ordered something.

"Coming up, *guapo*."

"So, what time does the band get here?" I asked.

"Oh, I love your accent," she cooed. "It gets me *so* hot!"

"Spare me, please," I moaned in English.

"Whadeber ju wan, beeg boy," she replied in more or less the same language, unfurling her tongue for my edification.

I couldn't wait to get home in order to, among other things, repeat this conversation to my wife. But I had to make one last stab at the band. Putting a hundred-peso bill on the bar, I said, "All I want is…"

"I don't care what you want," she said indignantly. "You won't get it here with a lousy hundred pesos."

At that moment the band staggered providentially in the door, taking seats at a large round table in the back. Wasting no time, I walked over and asked if I could buy them a round of drinks. No one demurred.

After we'd tasted our rum and cokes, I asked them how much they charged.

"Our normal fee is two thousand pesos an hour," the rather dusty accordion player said, naming an outrageous price.

"Let's be serious," I suggested. "If you want…"

"Next Saturday, did you say?" the guitar player broke in. "We have a *compromiso*. Can't make it."

"No, that's in two Saturdays, you castrated ox," the accordion player said.

"No, he's right," the drummer said.

"Who's right?"

"He is!"

"*Por favor! Por favor!*" I shouted.

After a while everyone settled down and we came to an understanding: four hours at $800 pesos an hour, plus all the food they could eat and enough booze to get happy, but not enough to get ridiculous.

As I was leaving, the problematic guitar player said, "What's your hurry? They got a girl upstairs with a pair of papayas on her you could live off for a week."

"Who's that?" the accordion player wanted to know.

"Lola."

"Ay Lola!" the bass player moaned. "Lola, *mi amor*! Lola, *mi pasion*! Lola, *mi...mi...*"

"I still think we have a *compromiso*," the guitar player shouted at my fleeing back. "We'll call you."

"So, everything is set?" Lucy asked me upon my return.

"Um, yes and no. We agreed to a deal, but the guitar player thought they might have a previous engagement. They said they'd call me to confirm."

"I hope there's no problem," Consuelo said anxiously.

"I wouldn't worry," I told her. "They were just playing hard to get." Unlike the barmaid, I thought. "How about some lunch?" I asked my wife.

"I'll make it," Consuelo offered. She was, I could see, grateful for the effort I had made to hire the band, and wanted to show her appreciation. "What would you like?"

"Just some tacos," I said.

"That's all?" Lucy asked. "Aren't you hungry?"

"Okay," I said, "toss in a side of penicillin."

My wife had a pretty good arm for a woman, but I had excellent reflexes, and the jar of hot sauce missed my head by half a meter.

Several days passed with no word from the band. The women were growing nervous. Remain calm, I urged them, the band is sure to call at any moment. Then, just three days before the party, we returned from a late dinner to find the message light blinking on the answering machine.

"That must be the band," Consuelo said breathlessly.

There were, in fact, several messages. The first featured a number of male voices, and was punctuated by bursts of loud music and the sound of glass breaking in the background.

"*Hello? Hello?*" the first voice said.

"*What's the matter?*" the second voice said. "*Isn't he home?*"

"*No, I think he's home. But...*"

"But what?"

"He says he's not there."

"What? How could he say he's not there? If he wasn't there, he couldn't talk to you."

"That's right," a third voice said. *"Only someone who's there could say that he wasn't there. It's only logical."*

"Logical? What do you know about logical, you son of a raped mother!"

Consuelo, a deeply religious woman, reached frantically for her rosary.

"Hey, shut your mouth, you red pubic hair," someone screamed, *"or I'll shut it for you!"*

"Oh yeah, I'd like to see you try, you lousy faggot!"

"You son of a diseased whore, it's a machine!" a fourth voice exclaimed.

"What's a machine?"

"It's a machine that's talking to you."

"A machine is talking to me?"

"Yes!"

"A talking machine? What have you been smoking, you rat-brained moron!"

(Sounds of glass breaking, accompanied by shouts, grunts and dull thuds.)

"Enough, you castrated ox-whores! We have important business to conduct."

"You sure this is the band you want?" I asked my wife.

"Okay, okay, everybody shut up! So what do we do?"

"Simple. The machine talks to you, you talk back."

"You want me to talk to a machine? What do I look like?"

"You look like the south end of a north bound burro!" someone shouted.

At this point, wild laughter was heard, followed by a great deal of confused shouting, which was followed in turn by the sound of more glass breaking. Then the line went dead.

The second message was from the barmaid, who seemed to be somewhat more familiar with answering machines than the musicians.

"Ay, guapo, that voice, it drives me wild! Please, I beg you, let me be your slave. I'll do anything you want. And so will Lola. We'll do things your wife never dreamed of. We'll ..."

The force with which I hit the delete button on the answering machine was so great it sent the apparatus flying off the table, into the next room and out the back door. Wisely, I followed suit.

Sow Sweet It Is!

ig burly Bob lumbered into the shop and made a bear-like bee-line for the exquisitely painted room divider standing in the corner.

"That sure is a beauty, eh?" he bellowed.

"Yes, it certainly is!" I fervently agreed from behind my desk.

"My name is Bob," the bearded man announced. "I'm from *Lonesome Beaver, Saskatchewan.*"

"That's a pretty…uh…unusual name," I replied.

"Maybe down here in Mexico it is," he said defensively, "but where I come from, there's all kinds of Bobs."

"Yes, of course," I said, favoring my hirsute client with a fearful look.

"I'm a pretty fair wood-worker myself," Bob boasted modestly, "and my brother is a darn good painter. Between us, we could make a divider just like that. Except for the finish. I've never seen one like it. There must be some kind of special technique they use."

Smiling enigmatically, I said, "There certainly is."

"I'd sure be obliged," Bob said, "if you could tell me exactly what that technique is. Then my brother and I could make one just like it. Eh?"

"Gee, Bob," I said gently, "I don't know how to tell you this, but the reason we have all this beautiful stuff here in the shop—stuff we have spent a great deal of time and money to obtain, I might add—is because we want to *sell* it."

"I realize that, and I respect that," Bob rumbled respectfully. "Especially since I'm a wood-worker myself."

Deciding that the huge bear-like man was probably several beers short of a six-pack, I said, "That's nice, Bob." Then I picked up a newspaper and began to peruse, with a sense of mounting urgency, the help-wanted pages.

"Mind if I have a seat?" Bob asked.

"Be my guest," I said graciously, and Bob settled, with little room to spare, into a beautifully hand-carved and painted chair directly in front of my desk.

"So I guess there's no way," he said with a faint note of menace in his voice, "I could convince you to tell me what the secret to getting that finish is. Eh?"

Outside of pointing a gun at my head, I don't think so, Bob, I thought to myself.

"Heck," I said aloud, "you seem like a pretty nice guy, Bob. Why not?"

"Hey, thanks a lot," Bob growled gratefully.

"Okay, Bob, the first thing is, you've got to make sure you've got some real sharp chisels. Nothing worse than working with a dull chisel."

"I know all about chiseling," Bob said, beginning to lose his temper. "Didn't I tell you that I'm a wood..."

"Sorry," I cut in apologetically, "I forgot—you're an expert chiseller, aren't you?"

"It's the secret of the finish I need to know," Bob reminded me.

"Okay, Bob," I said, lowering my voice to a conspiratorial whisper, "the secret is, before painting the wood, you've got to soak it in pig urine for at least a month."

"*What?*"

"Hard to believe, eh?" I said, shaking my head in amazement. "The entire process is an old and closely guarded secret which has been passed down from generation to generation, starting with the *Mayans*, continuing with the *Aztecs* and ending with the *Mocha Javans*. You know, Bob, I really shouldn't be telling you all this, but you seem like such a nice guy."

"*Pig urine?* Just pig urine?" Bob said dubiously.

"No, not just any pig urine, Bob," I said soberly. "It has to come from the female of the species, what's known as the sow."

"I don't believe it."

"I know how you feel, Bob. I didn't believe it either; not until I'd seen it with my own eyes, and smelled it with my own nose."

"But how do they collect enough? They must need gallons of it."

"A lot of artisans are also farmers, Bob," I said truthfully. "And the particular artisan who makes our furniture," I added with somewhat less veracity, "is a pig farmer."

"But still," Bob demanded, "how does he get them…"

"It's a remarkable procedure, Bob. He trains the female pigs (who are more intelligent than dogs, but not quite as bright as Registered Republicans) to urinate into special troughs."

"Yeah, I've heard that pigs are awful smart," Bob agreed. "So how do I get my hands on some of this stuff?"

"Well…"

With no clear idea how to answer Bob's last question, I was about to bolt for the bathroom when Don Arturo, an octogenarian I had known for over twenty years, walked in the door toting a pair of unlabeled liter bottles. The bottles were filled to the brim with a dubious-looking liquid, and capped with home-made corncob corks.

Don Arturo had the largest pair of ears you are ever likely to see on a human being—old leathery ears which protruded preposterously out from beneath his battered straw hat like a pair of baseball gloves. With his hat, overalls and worn-out huaraches, he looked every inch the rural farmer, which in fact he was. At one time Don Arturo had made the finest *raicilla* in Jalisco, and I had been his loyal customer. But over the years, as his mental faculties had declined, so had the quality of his moonshine. It had in fact deteriorated to the point where the excruciatingly foul smell alone was enough to give a grown possum the dry heaves.

"What incredible luck!" I cried. "It's the man himself!"

"You mean..." Bob began, unable to believe his good fortune.

"Yes, yes!" I shouted gleefully. "It's the man who made the divider, and it looks like he's..."

At this point I switched to Spanish, addressing Don Arturo, inquiring after his health and that of his forty-six grandchildren. After assuring me that every one of them (with the exception of the youngest, a homicidal bus driver) was just fine, the ancient bootlegger proudly raised aloft (like an actor who has just won a pair of Oscars) the two bottles of *raicilla*.

"The best I ever made," he beamed toothlessly. "You can have both liters for only three hundred pesos."

"Bob," I said, switching back to English, "you have got to be the luckiest man who ever lived. Don Arturo here is desperate for some cash and needs to sell two liters of what he says is the best batch he's ever had."

"Why the best?" Bob asked.

Good question.

"The sows were in heat," I said, miraculously managing to keep a straight face. "Gives it extra-added strength."

"How much does he want?" Bob asked.

"Are those new shoes?" I asked Don Arturo in Spanish.

After looking down at his feet for a while, he said, yes they were. He'd only had them for five years.

"It's kind of high," I told Bob, "due to the pigs being in heat and all: five hundred pesos a bottle."

"That does seem high," Bob said knowledgeably, as if he'd just looked up the price of pig urine futures that morning on the Chicago Mercantile Exchange.

"If it's too much, don't worry," I said helpfully. "I'll take them myself. I've got a couple of chairs that need refinishing and..."

"I didn't say it was too much," Bob protested. "I just said it was kind of high. Can I, uh, *check it out* before I pay for it?"

"Sure thing." Snatching a liter from Don Arturo, I pulled the cork and handed the bottle to Bob, who took a tentative sniff and nearly lost his lunch all over my antique desk.

"Oh, that smells…that smells…*terrible!*" he croaked.

"Well naturally, Bob," I said serenely. "I mean, it's not exactly *Chanel Number Five.* Eh?"

Customer Service

For reasons best explained by someone with a degree in Abnormal Psychology, I recently decided to go out and purchase a DVD player, a device about as familiar to me as the flora on Uranus. Before spending my hard-earned pesos, I thought it prudent to seek some expert advice.

Larry, my hi-tech guru, was not an easy man to locate, except on Monday nights during football season, when he was reliably parked at the same table in *El Burrito*, swilling beers and rooting for whoever happened to be losing the game. By always rooting for the losing team, Larry explained, he was able to consistently work up a good head of frustration atop the *Bud Lite* of his psyche.

"I'm too laidback," Larry told me. "I need to piss myself off at least once a week, just to keep my edge."

Larry's lack of edge was understandable, spending as he did the majority of his waking life smoking pot and having online sex with virtual hookers.

The game that night featured a group of homicidal steroidally enhanced young assassins from a cold northern state pummeling into submission a group of like-minded creatures from a warm southern state. Somehow the fact that the two teams came from distinct geographical regions was supposed to motivate the viewer into pulling for one of them or the other. In reality, with both teams slogging along at the bottom of their respective divisions, no one (not even the players' parents) had any serious interest in the outcome.

"Good game?" I asked, taking a seat beside Larry.

"Terrible," Larry replied, slamming down his beer. "My team is losing."

"Which is your team?" I asked. Larry was from Canada, and so immune to American geographical rivalries.

"The one with less points," he said with disgust.

Having thus exhausted all potential topics of mutual interest, I got to the point. "Larry, what do you know about DVDs?"

"Everything there is to know, which isn't much."

"So, which brand do you recommend?"

"They're all the same," Larry grunted. "Just buy the cheapest one whose name you can pronounce."

The next day found me at our neighborhood Wal-Mart cruising the DVD aisle. It was not difficult to locate the cheapest brand. There was a small mountain of them piled against a pillar, and the brand name was one which seemed comfortably familiar, not to mention Japanese. I made my purchase, went home, removed the device from its box and began to peruse the instruction manual.

This monument to Asian inscrutability had been helpfully translated into both English and Spanish. Making no sense of the Spanish section, I turned quickly to the English one, only to discover that it made even less sense. The Byzantine instructions for connecting the DVD to the TV, for example, appeared to have been written by someone who was at once sadistic, dyslexic and only vaguely familiar with the English language:

"If your connect the player to a monitors or projectors having the component video input connectors, they conform to the output signals from the Component Video Out (Y, CB / B-Y+R=Y) connectors on the player, which making the connection of the component via the Component Video Out connectors using three video cords connecting (*Not supplied!*) of the same kind, you will get a better picture."

Of course. A better picture. Who in their right senses would not want a better picture?

Two hours later having, in a fit of high-tech rage, shredded, stomped and peed upon the remains of the instruction manual, I set about connecting my DVD player utilizing the oldest scientific method of them all: trial and error. This took only an hour. Then I turned on the television, inserted a disc into the player and waited for something to happen. Naturally, nothing did.

It was then that I made several discouraging discoveries. My DVD was manufactured, not in Japan, but in China, and the imported DVD I'd inserted only worked in something called *Region I*, whereas Puerto Vallarta was, apparently, located in the very heart of *Region IV*. In China, I had recently read, the average skilled worker makes the equivalent of seventeen cents a month, almost as much as a *Wal-Mart* supervisor.

In any case, after procuring a Region IV-compatible DVD; after accidentally learning that there was a button on the television I had to press three times in a row to make that instrument receptive to the signals coming from the DVD player; after unwillingly sitting through the PREVIEW of the movie I was attempting to watch sixteen times, I must have finally pressed (by accident, again) a fatal series of buttons on the remote control. The picture began to cascade vertically up and down the screen, making me nauseous.

Unable to correct this flaw, I returned with the device to the customer service counter at Wal-Mart, where, after waiting twenty minutes for the representative to finish with a previous *contretemps*, I was told to wait some more while "technical support personnel" were summoned to the scene.

"That's not really necessary," I told her. "If you would just give me a new machine—one that works—I'll be on my way."

"That's not possible," she said. Then, retrieving a microphone (manufactured in China), she made a store-wide call for technical support persons, who did not appear. Four further amplified pleas finally produced the indicated individual, a seventeen-year-old girl who appeared to be frightened to death of anything with wires hanging from it.

Together we carted my machine over to the electronics section, where we found a large television all plugged-in and ready to receive my recalcitrant DVD into its electronic embrace. Our first (and only, it turned out) problem was the seeming inability of the tech expert to compatibly connect the two machines. She finally called over her supervisor, a young man who, though only months away from needing his first shave, possessed a degree of *ennui* well beyond his youthful years.

Only then was I permitted to watch in disbelief as the two of them, after first dropping my remote control on the floor (twice) attempted (unsuccessfully) to discover the correct combination of connections, the one which would magically produce a DVD-inspired image to appear on the screen of the television. A half an hour of this torture was about all I could stand, so I made a suggestion. "Why don't you just give me a new one?"

"We will," the young man said in a bored voice, "but first we have to make sure that your machine is actually defective."

"And how do you propose to do that," I asked, gritting my teeth, "if you can't even figure out how to plug the miserable thing in?"

Much to his credit, the young man gave my question a considerable amount of thought. Finally, he said, "I'll have to call my supervisors."

"*Supervisors?*" I shrieked. "You mean there's two of them?"

"Yes."

"And how long," I snarled, "do you suppose it will take to get *Beavis and Butthead* over here?"

"You watch *MTV*?" he asked with a sudden burst of excitement.

"Only when I'm feeling particularly brain-dead," I replied.

"Me, too," he said. "Hey, you're pretty cool. For an old guy."

And that was when I realized that there was in fact no hope, no hope whatsoever.

Vocational Gruel

Over the years I have been deluged with literally three or four requests from faithful fans desperate to know what I was like as a young man. In order to remove this particular primate from my sagging back once and for all, I hereby offer the lurid details of my most unforgettable adolescent moment.

Back in the early 1960's students all over the USA were routinely subjected to a form of torture known as the "Standardized Test". The idea of being *standardized* (lumped together into some amorphous grouping with kids I didn't even know) was something I could not abide. And so, with Gandhi as my guide, I began a one-man movement which came to be known as *CNC*: Creative Non-Cooperation.

My first act as *CNC* involved a standardized English multiple-choice test with a hundred questions. Sharpening my No. 2 pencil with leaden determination I resolved, whatever the cost, to answer all of the questions incorrectly.

But achieving this lofty goal proved to be more difficult than I'd expected. When the scores came back, I had, much to my chagrin, marked one of the questions with an acceptable answer.

I had also caused the primitive computer analyzing my score to suffer a binary breakdown. A score of one percent was, by the rules of its limited logic, statistically impossible, and the poor mechanical brain, unable to deal with this numerical anomaly, had gone into a deep funk, refusing to communicate with its human handlers for nearly a week.

Shortly thereafter, our entire junior class was given the most insidious standardized examination of them all, the *Kuder Preference Test*, the results of which were supposed to help guide our unsteady young hands when it came time for choosing a career.

For each question we were given three choices, and told to punch a hole through the little circle opposite the choice we liked the most, and another through the one which appealed to us the least.

A typical example: A: Garbage Man B: Engineer C: Nurse.

Or: A: Visit a Sick Friend B: Play Softball C: Write a letter.

It did not take me long to figure out what the misguided individuals who had designed this educational abomination were up to, and I decided at once to do everything in my power to thwart their nefarious plans.

The test had no time limit and long after everyone else had finished, I was still hard at work. The teacher, impressed by my unaccustomed display of diligence, complimented me on my new-found test-taking intensity.

"Miss Smoot," I told the confused woman, "this is going to be my multiple-choice masterpiece!"

One week later I was called into the office of the school guidance counselor, a heavily under-worked man named Mr. Blaine. Mr. Blaine and I had had several face-to-faces already, always at his insistence, during which the term "under-achiever" was launched at me with repetitive futility, like a shuttlecock in a poorly played game of badminton.

On this occasion Mr. Blaine was accompanied by the school principal, Mr. Noyes, who, if the truth be known, was not my biggest booster. Between the two of them they proceeded to explain to me that the idiotic *Kuder Preference Test* had built into it something called a *Validity Score*. For the test to have any practical value, one had to have a *Validity Score* over forty-seven. Such a score indicated that there was indeed some type of "logical consistency" to the Testee's responses; that taken together they did in fact form a "pattern" from which certain inclinations could then be "reasonably deduced". For example: you wouldn't mind being a lawyer, but the odds were you'd feel less than fulfilled working as a cesspool cleaner.

Out of the four hundred and twenty-five members of the junior class, Mr. Blaine informed me, only two students had failed to achieve a *Validity Score* over forty-seven.

"Don't tell me I was one of them?" I asked, aghast.

"Your *Validity Score* was fifteen!" the principal roared with outrage. "No one has ever scored that low in the entire history of the United States!"

"You're making the whole school look bad," Mr. Blaine remarked.

"You have to take it again," Mr. Noyes decreed, "and this time you better score above forty-seven. Or else!"

I was then led to another room and left alone with a blank test book, and the only other student who had failed to validate Mr. Kuder's absurd creation. Not surprisingly, the other student was my best friend, Andy, who had amassed a *Validity Score* of thirty-five.

Though Andy was my best friend and I loved him like a brother, the general consensus (to which I too subscribed) was that he was essentially insane. He was, in fact, shunned by almost everyone in the school, despite the fact that he would grow up to become our most renowned alumni, a world-famous performer whose tragically shortened life was eventually transmuted to the silver screen.

"We both flunked the test!" Andy giggled.

"Good job!" I said, shaking his hand.

"Now what do we do?" Andy asked. "They told me if we don't pass it this time, we're getting detention."

"Okay, Andy, the thing to do, if you want to pass this test, is to answer the questions honestly."

"I did."

"Oh."

"Did you say you wanted to be a dog-catcher," Andy wondered, "or you didn't want to be a dog-catcher?"

"I can't remember. Look, Andy, here's what you do. Every time they have something about math or science, punch the 'I like it the most' tab. That ought to do it."

"But I hate math and science. I want to have a children's TV show, like Buffalo Bob."

"I know, Andy, but the idiots who designed this test did not make any provisions for kids like you who want to grow up and be Buffalo Bob. So you'll have to lie."

"That would be dishonest," Andy pointed out.

"It's that or detention, my friend."

"I can't have detention. There's an Elvis Presley Film Festival in the City next week, and I can't miss a single movie. Do you want to go?"

"No, Andy, I hate Elvis movies; they're stupid."

"They are not stupid!" Andy declared.

"Yes, they are…wait a minute; that's it. Music! Just put a hole through all the music questions, and forget the rest of them."

"Fine," Andy said, favoring me with his trademark blank stare.

A week later I was called back to Mr. Blaine's office, where I was greeted with an enormous frown.

"You don't look too happy, Mr. Blaine," I said pleasantly.

"Congratulations!" he said, his voice oozing sarcasm. "Now you're the *only* student in the school without a valid *Validity Score*!"

"You mean," I asked in astonishment, "Andy passed and I didn't?"

"Your friend squeaked by with a forty-nine."

"And I…"

"Twenty-six." Mr. Blaine spat out the number with disgust, as if it were one of those sexually transmitted diseases they were always warning us about in Health Class.

"That's really strange, Mr. Blaine. I admit, the first time I took the test I was not being entirely candid. But this time I answered all the questions as honestly as I could."

"You did?"

"I swear."

Mr. Blaine, who sometimes did double-duty as a substitute gym teacher, deflated like a punctured volley ball before my very eyes. "What a waste," he muttered sadly, "what a waste."

"I couldn't agree with you more, Mr. Blaine," I said with emotion. "Just to make that stupid test, they probably cut down half the trees in Oregon."

A Prescription For Disaster

As I sat imprisoned in my wife's wonderful shop thinking up ways to get myself fired, a particularly insane idea came to me in the form of a marketing concept so devoid of common sense it made my nose hairs unfurl with admiration.

For several minutes I sat there wondering if this new scheme might finally prod my wife into granting me my most fervent desire: being banned (permanently) from her shop. On the other hand, it could easily backfire. In the past some of my more injudicious ideas had proved to be highly counter-productive. In several lamentable instances, they had actually *increased* sales. Finally I decided I had nothing to lose, except my testicles, which had been in deep storage for the past eight years anyway. I would, like the *Viagra* commercial says, "Just do it!"

On our annual buying trip the previous summer we had come upon a sensational deal on beautifully hand-painted wooden pillboxes. They were elegant, skillfully crafted and *really cheap*! Momentarily carried away by my good fortune, I'd purchased ten thousand of them which, I admit, was probably overdoing it a bit.

Upon our return to Vallarta in October, we put the pillboxes on display and to our satisfaction they sold quite briskly (about four a week), but not quite briskly enough. At that rate, it would take us approximately seventy-three years to sell every pillbox, a timeframe which did not bode well for our early retirement plans.

In order to increase sales, I reasoned, these pillboxes need to be personalized. They need a name, something our clients can sink their teeth into. But what name? Was there a name that your average North American would readily associate with a pillbox?

Why yes, of course there was!

Wasting no time I made a sign and placed it in the window. The very next client to walk in the door (a Mrs. Smith from Kline, Wisconsin) read the sign and said, "*The Rush Limbaugh Pillbox*. Very clever. I'll take twenty-seven."

Mrs. Smith was followed by a steady stream of customers who, after chuckling over my little joke, proceeded to pick up one or more of their very own *Rush Limbaugh Pillboxes*. Growing more depressed by the minute, I realized that my marketing strategy was not having its desired effect.

Then a Mr. Bristol from Meyers, Texas, strode bowlegged up to my desk, where he said, "I just saw that sign hangin' in your window."

"Yes," I said dully, "how many pillboxes would you like?"

"I'm not buyin' nothin'," Mr. Bristol drawled unpleasantly.

"Thank God!" I sighed.

"I just want to tell you how much I disapprove of that sign."

"You mean, you're offended?" I asked hopefully.

"Yes, I am."

"Would you like to fill out an official complaint form?" I asked eagerly.

"No, I don't want to fill out any forms," he said with irritation. "I just want you to know, that as a Rush Limbaugh fan, I find your sign…"

"Wait a minute. Don't tell me you're an actual Rush Limbaugh fan?" I asked, my mouth agape with disbelief.

"I certainly am," the man declared, "and proud of it!"

"Gosh," I said, "I didn't think they let you people out of the country."

"What's that supposed to mean?" Mr. Bristol demanded.

"Well," I said, "don't you Rush Limbaugh fans hate everybody who's not exactly like you are?"

"Exactly like we are?" Mr. Bristol repeated, eyeing me with suspicion.

"Yeah, you know," I explained, "white, intolerant, under-educated, white, frustrated, angry, white, paranoid…"

"Now, you wait just one minute," Mr. Bristol interrupted me. "I'll have you know that Mr. Limbaugh has millions of followers."

"So did Adolph Hitler," I pointed out pleasantly. "Sir, could you please excuse me for a moment; I have to wait on some real customers."

The shop had filled with clients, mostly women I knew from previous visits. As Mr. Bristol stood off to one side, apparently waiting to bushwhack me again at the earliest opportunity, a Mrs. Lily from Eli, Wisconsin, approached my desk.

"What a delightful idea," she chirped, "I'll take four Rush Limbaugh pillboxes. But don't total me up yet, I want to get one of those beautiful rugs."

"Certainly," I said dejectedly.

"Like I was sayin'," Mr. Bristol said, sidling back up to the desk, "makin' fun of someone's medical problem is just plain bad taste. If I was you I'd take that sign down and toss it in the trash, where it belongs."

"I don't know," I replied judiciously, "I guess we just don't have the same tolerant attitude towards drug addicts down here like you open-minded folks up there in Texas."

"Drug addict?" Mr. Bristol shouted. "He's no drug addict! The man has a back problem and…"

"And acquired prescription drugs illegally, a crime by the way, Sr. Bristol, and one which Rush himself said should *always* be punished with jail time."

"He committed no crime," Sr. Bristol insisted. "He had a prescription."

"He had about a thousand prescriptions," I pointed out, "nine hundred and ninety-nine of them illegal. But I'll tell you what. Let's do the democratic thing and take a poll— you believe in Democracy, don't you?"

"Democracy?" the man from Meyers, Texas, said uncertainly.

"Yeah," I said, "democracy—you know: one idiot, one vote. Good morning, Mrs. Sandoz," I called out to a customer across the shop. "What do you think of Rush Limbaugh?"

"Rush Limbaugh?" she said, as she tried on an elegant pair of chandelier earrings. "That racist moron! They ought to put a muzzle on him."

"That's just one person's opinion," Sr. Bristol drawled. "I happen to come from Rush Limbaugh country, and nobody thinks like that up there."

"Well, let's try someone else," I said. "Oh, Mrs. Bayer? What do you think of Rush Limbaugh?"

Mrs. Bayer was trying on a lovely cotton shawl from Oaxaca. "Rush Limbaugh," she said with disgust, "that sick bag of human refuse belongs behind bars, along with all his feeble-minded followers!"

"Mrs. Bayer," I asked in alarm, "are you saying that *all* of Mr. Limbaugh's fans are feeble-minded?"

"Well," she replied, "all I can say is, anyone who believes the sewage that spews from that hate-monger's mouth has to be several helmets short of a football team. By the way, I'll take nine pillboxes."

"Coming right up, Mrs. Bayer. Well," I said, turning to Mr. Bristol, "it looks like your big hero isn't terribly popular around here."

"Yeah, well, he's got twenty million regular listeners," he replied combatively. "And twenty million people can't be wrong!"

"Says who?" Mrs. Sandoz called out. "Not everyone gets to be bright—even in a democracy."

Dress For Duress

Once again, our landlady was desperately in need of funds.

"What else is new?" I asked her.

The only solvent member of her entire extended family, Teresa was constantly coming to me, her principle source of income, with an astonishing variety of "urgent situations" which could only be successfully resolved with immediate infusions of cash. Over the years I had advanced her money to repair a fallen roof, amputate a sister's foot, pay her property taxes, send a niece on vacation to Guatemala, and so on.

"This time," Teresa said, ignoring my frivolous question, "I'm going to give you an especially good deal, if you and Lucy could pay, say, a year's rent in advance."

"Teresa," I reminded her gently, "our rent is already paid for the next year. Don't you remember? Your cousin's truck caught fire and…"

"Yes, yes," I know," Teresa said impatiently. "1997 is paid in full. That's why I'm going to make you such a good deal for 1998. 1998 I'm practically giving away."

"I don't know, Teresa. Paying two years in advance, given the circumstances, seems a bit risky right now."

"If I don't get the money in the next two days," Teresa said, playing her ace, "Roberto is going to jail."

Roberto was her younger brother.

"What do you mean? Isn't he a policeman?"

"Yes."

"Well, how does a policeman wind up in jail?"

"By killing someone," Teresa replied with an astonishing matter-of-factness. "But it wasn't his fault," she added loyally.

"You mean it was an accident?"

"More or less. The problem is, he was off-duty at the time. If he had shot the man while on-duty, he could have got off with just a warning. As it is, we thought we had the judge all taken care of, but then, all of a sudden, the *cabrón* doubled the fine."

"The *fine*? There's a *fine* for murder?"

"It was an accident," Teresa said without conviction.

"Teresa, you know I've never turned you down before."

"Yes, you've always been very good to me."

"And you to us," I said sincerely. "But what with the property up for sale and everything…"

"It is *not* for sale," she said defensively.

"Yes, that's what you tell us. But all these realtors keep coming around and it's making us nervous."

"Forget the realtors," she grunted dismissively, "they're a bunch of idiots."

I did not want to argue with Teresa, but there was no getting around the fact that the realtors, whatever their level of mental acuity, really *believed* that the property on which our rented beach house stood was up for sale. On the other hand, the government and Teresa's family had been fighting over this prime piece of beachfront property for more than twenty years. The resulting flood of lawsuits, feints, false alarms, pseudo-sales and court orders had helped to wean an entire litter of lawyers, while at the same time resolving absolutely nothing.

Who really owned the property? Was it Teresa's family? Was it the government? Was it the Archbishop of Canterbury? As I write these words, almost a decade after the fact, the two sides are still duking it out, with no end in sight.

Finally I told Teresa I would get back to her in twenty-four hours, and to give Roberto my best regards.

Lucy was less than eager, despite the extraordinarily good deal we'd been offered, to hand over another year's rent. "That last realtor was pretty sure of himself," she reminded me.

"Yeah, and you made short work of him, honey," I said with husbandly pride.

A month earlier a realtor, with a trio of investors in tow, had appeared unannounced at our front door. After introducing himself, the well-groomed salesman asked if he could take a quick look at the house.

"What for?" Lucy demanded.

"Well, you must know," he replied patronizingly, "that this whole property is for sale."

"I must know no such thing," Lucy said.

"Yes, well it definitely is for sale, and these folks have come all the way from Mexico City to see it, so if it wouldn't be too much trouble...?"

At this point the realtor made the serious mistake of actually squeezing his way into the house, thereby placing himself immediately and forever on the family *caca* list. Moments later his little group squeezed in behind him, like a trio of anxious ducklings waddling after their mother.

As they began to swarm about our living room, Lucy said in a loud voice, "I can't imagine who would be stupid enough to buy this property when the title's been in dispute for over twenty years."

"What's that?" one of the investors asked in alarm.

"Oh, that was all settled long ago," the salesman said hurriedly.

"Settled?" Lucy laughed. "This place has more lawsuits attached to it than an asbestos factory."

"That is a gross exaggeration," the salesman muttered angrily.

"You never mentioned anything about any lawsuits," the investor complained.

"The title has so many holes in it," Lucy said, making colorful but confused use of her idiomatic Spanish, "you could drive a truck of Swiss cheese through it."

"We are very sorry to have troubled you," the realtor said with a forced smile, gathering his clients together and herding them towards the door.

"No trouble," Lucy said graciously to their retreating behinds. "Careful where you step now; it's scorpion season and we haven't fumigated for two days."

Not surprisingly, that particular realtor never returned. But we knew in our heart of hearts that there would be others. What we did not know was whether or not the property was actually for sale.

"We can't just hand over another year's rent," Lucy insisted. "We have to find out what's really going on."

"Don't worry, honey," I said reassuringly, "I have a plan."

Bernie, our eighty-year-old neighbor, was watching *CNN* and partaking of his first Mai Tai of the afternoon when I walked unannounced into his living room.

"Hey neighbor, how the hell are you?" he croaked. "You're just in time for *Moneyline*. Want a Mai Tai?"

Bernie was retired navy and prone to mental confusion. At times he appeared to suffer from the misapprehension that he had retired to Hawaii, instead of Puerto Vallarta.

"Man those trade winds are really blowing today," he went on. "Market's down," he added in the next breath, as if the two phenomena were somehow related.

"I'll pass on the drink, Bernie. But I do need a small favor."

"What's that?" he asked suspiciously.

"I need to borrow a tie."

"A tie? Who died?"

"No one died, Bernie. I have an appointment and…It's a little difficult to explain."

"I've lived on this island for twenty years," Bernie proclaimed, "and the only time I've worn a tie is for funerals. You have an appointment, you say? You're going to look like a goddamn idiot wearing a tie."

"That's kind of the idea."

"You want to look like an idiot?"

"More or less."

"Want a Mai Tai?"

"No, just a tie."

"I've only got two of 'em anymore," Bernie sighed. "And one I can't lend out, in case somebody drops dead all of a sudden. The other one's a little loud."

"That's fine. As long as it's clean."

"Clean? I wouldn't know. And neither would anybody else. Wait right here."

Bernie was correct. The atrocious multi-hued monstrosity could have been splattered with the entire contents of a high school cafeteria, and no one would have been any the wiser.

Back at the house, I unearthed a shirt that would "go" with the tie: a tacky candy-striped short-sleeved sport shirt, which I had worn only once—during the Nixon Administration. Naturally, it was far too tight around the neck, and getting that last button closed required a team effort.

"How do I look?" I asked Lucy, once my costume was complete."

"Like a total geek," she said.

"Gee, thanks."

"I meant," she sighed, "like the geek of my dreams."

Arriving at the appropriate governmental office, I cleared my constricted throat and announced to the receptionist in the most grotesque Spanish accent I could muster (Joe Pesci meets José Jimenez) that I was interested in the large beachfront chunk of land for sale across the way. A young mid-level bureaucrat was quickly summoned and I went into my prepared spiel.

"I represent a group of American doctors," I told the young man, "who need to invest, for tax purposes, in a large real estate project. We have been eyeing a tract in Cabo San Lucas, but are also interested in the beachfront parcel across the street. The cost is not all that important, since the doctors need to invest a great deal of money."

Halfway through my little speech the young man began to drool with anticipation. By the time I had finished he was leading me to the "VIP" room, where I was offered a nice plush chair, served coffee and cake, and told to please make myself at home.

The weak coffee, little more than discolored water really, was awful. But the cake was excellent. I was just finishing my third slice, in fact, when a covey of covetous *caballeros* with dollar signs superimposed over their pupils bustled purposefully into the room.

When everyone was seated around the small mahogany conference table, *El Jefe*, a Sr. Gutierrez, said, "So, I am told you are interested in the spectacular property next to Las Playeras Hotel."

Vigorously nodding my head, like the over-anxious nerd I was attempting to portray, I repeated the story about the doctors in search of a tax shelter. Sr. Gutierrez ordered one of his assistants to pass him a file, which he opened and handed to me. It contained a plot map of the property with all of the dimensions written in. Tiny palm trees had also been drawn upon the map, but I noticed that none of the houses were indicated.

"Very nice, Sr. Gut-terrace," I said, badly mispronouncing his name, "but, of course, the important thing is the price."

Several knowing looks were exchanged among the assistants.

"Yes," Sr. Gutierrez said, "we are asking four hundred dollars a meter. Four hundred times thirteen thousand two hundred meters comes to…"

"Five million, two hundred and eighty thousand dollars," I interrupted him. Smiling at their stunned faces I said with nerdish pride, "I've always had a good head for figures."

In reality, I had known the price for months.

"Yes, you certainly do," Sr. Gutierrez said. "We feel that this is a fair…"

"That's cheap, Sr. Gut-terrace," I interrupted him again. "But if you want to give it away, that's your business."

My rudeness, not to mention my repeated mispronunciation of his name, was I could see beginning to really wear on Sr. Gutierrez's nerves. But with a brave effort he managed to hide his displeasure behind a painfully forced smile.

"As I was saying," he purred, "we believe it is a fair price. What exactly, if you don't mind my asking, did the group you represent have in mind as far as development of the property is concerned?"

"Oh, that isn't really important," I said. "The main thing is getting rid of all this cash." For an instant I allowed my eyes to wander down to my briefcase, as if it were stuffed with the legal tender I had just referred to, and not with old copies of the *Mexico City News*.

"For such a great location," I went on, "there are many possibilities. I'm sure we can come up with something. A clinic, maybe, or a Recuperation Hotel," I adlibbed wildly.

For several moments there was total silence, as everyone struggled not to stare at the briefcase. "It's not a problem, is it?" I asked anxiously.

"What? What's not a problem?" Sr. Gutierrez asked, mirroring my anxiety.

"Paying with cash, Sr. Guitar-case. I hope that's not a problem."

"No, no, no. Not a problem," he smiled benignly.

"Okey-dokey," I said, pretending to study the plot map. "I think I'm ready to proceed with the purchase. I just have one question."

"Of course. That is what we are here for, to answer your questions."

"I have a small confession to make, Sr. Guitar-case," I said, smiling sheepishly.

"A confession?" he asked warily.

"Yes. Earlier today I took a good long walk all around the property, and I noticed something which could be a potential problem. There are people living there, Sr. Gutterrace. In houses! What about *them*? Are they going to give us a problem when it's time to take possession?"

"No, no, no problem." Sr. Gutierrez laughed indulgently.

"But what if they refuse to leave?" I persisted.

"Oh, we'll just get rid of them," he said light-heartedly.

"Get rid of them?" I repeated, raising my eyebrows in alarm. "You don't mean you'd kill them, do you?"

Sr. Gutierrez stopped smiling. "No, of course not. This is, after all, a civilized country. We'll just throw them out. By the way," he added, in a pathetically transparent attempt at changing the subject, "I've been admiring your tie. Do you know where I could get one?"

"Here," I said, removing the atrocity from around my constricted neck, "you can have it."

"No, I couldn't possibly," Sr. Gutierrez protested.

"No, I insist," I said, thrusting it into his hands. "We'll call it a downpayment on the deal."

It's a Wonderful Life?

People are always telling me how fortunate I am, what a wonderful life I lead. Well, I suppose there is some truth in that. Living in Puerto Vallarta, taking four-month-long working vacations, traveling all over Mexico collecting fine folk-art for the shop—it's not a bad way to pass the time by any means. But people don't see the other side of the coin, the downside of owning and operating a successful and highly acclaimed retail establishment.

Yesterday was a perfect example.

A man dressed in violently colored Bermuda shorts entered the shop and said, "You know, I was in Oaxaca once and these painted wooden animals you're selling were much cheaper there."

"Really?" I inquired politely. "When was that?"

"About thirty years ago."

The savvy traveler was replaced a few minutes later by an anxious couple from Indiana who seemed to think they had landed, not in a beach resort, but rather on some alien and hostile planet. After pretending to be interested in a beautiful hand-woven cotton shawl (a total steal at only ten dollars), they asked me if it was safe to eat, drink, walk and/or breathe in Puerto Vallarta. I assured them that it was, whereupon they backed nervously out the door.

My next customer actually bought something, a two-dollar tin Christmas ornament, but only after asking me if that was my best price.

Then my accountant, who I am always happy to see, stopped by. "I have some bad news," he said.

"What else is new?"

"Remember that citation you received two years ago for not making a payment which you actually did make?"

"How could I forget."

"Well, you're going to have to pay a fine."

"For what?"

"For not responding to the erroneous complaint on time."

"Wait a minute, Carlos, let me see if I understand this correctly. Even though we made the payment on time, we're being fined for not responding punctually to the false claim that we didn't?"

"That is correct. You know, I think you're really getting a good handle on how things work here."

"Things *work* here?"

"A figure of speech."

Carlos was followed thirty minutes later by a representative of the Chamber of Commerce who wanted me to give him five hundred pesos.

"What for?" I demanded.

"For all the work we do promoting your business," he replied with a straight face.

"For example?"

"For example, what?"

"Thanks, but I think I'll pass."

"You can't pass," he said, "the payment is not optional."

"One second," I said, "I want to call my accountant." When I got Carlos on the phone I asked him if the payment was really mandatory.

His reply: "Yes, and no."

"What do you mean, yes and no, Carlos? It has to be one or the other."

"Well, technically, it is optional," my accountant explained. "But, in reality, you have to pay it."

"Why is that, Carlos?"

"It's, uh, kind of complicated," he replied.

By noon I had grown substantially poorer, not to mention increasingly nauseous, due to some "sewer rehabilitation" work they were doing up the street. But then my "big sale of the day" walked in, a couple from Chicago who proceeded to purchase several extraordinarily beautiful *alebriges*, as well as two museum-quality masks. While my assistant was expertly packing their purchases, the husband handed me his credit card, which I swiped through the terminal, only to receive a flashing message which read: "CARD STOLEN: CALL THE POLICE IMMEDIATELY!"

When I explained, as politely and vaguely as possible, that there was a "small problem" with his credit card, the husband (who like most husbands absolutely despised the very idea of shopping) tore the card out of my hand, called me an unrepeatable name and stormed out of the shop. His wife, hugely embarrassed by her spouse's crude behavior, made a quick apology and fled the scene as well.

Bursting at the seams with good cheer now, I was set upon by a gentleman from Nova Scotia who wished to purchase a three-dollar hand-woven, naturally dyed woolen coaster. "You only want *one coaster*?" I asked in disbelief.

"I live by myself," he explained.

"Okay," I sighed, "that'll be thirty pesos."

"Not so fast," he said. "I haven't definitely made up my mind one hundred percent yet. To be honest, the price seems kind of high."

"Kind of high?"

"Yes. I'm thinking of offering you two dollars Canadian for it," he said, "but I'd like to know a little more about how it's made before I make a final decision."

"I'm sorry, sir," I said respectfully, "but we don't bargain here. We have excellent prices, and they're fixed—just like our cats."

"Is that right?" he said. "Okay, I'll give you fourteen pesos then."

By this time several women were attempting to approach my desk with merchandise and money in their hands, but the gentleman from Nova Scotia stood blocking their way.

"Sir, I repeat, we do not bargain here. If you'll excuse me, these ladies would like to…"

"I'll give you fifteen pesos," he said, "that's my last offer."

"Sir. Read my lips: We…don't…bargain!"

"Sixteen pesos."

"Listen. You make me one more ridiculous offer and the price doubles."

"Seventeen pesos."

"Okay, you asked for it. Now that coaster is going to cost you sixty pesos."

"You can't do that," he shouted. "The price is only thirty."

"It *was* thirty," I growled, "but now it's sixty. Take it or leave it."

Clutching the coaster tightly in his fist, the man tossed thirty pesos onto my desk and ran from the store.

"Have a nice day!" I called after him.

"My, that man was rude," one of the women remarked.

"Well," I said indulgently, "perhaps he hasn't heard."

"Heard what?"

"It's a wonderful life."

Kitty Litter Lunch

After well over a thousand superlative dining adventures, the law of gastronomical averages finally caught us up. And I am not talking about a lackluster lunch, or a disagreeable dinner: I am talking about the culinary equivalent of Custard's Last Stand!

Pedro's Hideaway (not concealed quite well enough, as it turned out) was located on the 900 block of *calle Augustin Hernandez*. Lucy and I stumbled upon it quite by accident while searching the back roads of Vallarta for a *Kitty Litter Outlet Store*. When our car broke down in front of what looked like a decent place to eat, we decided to give it a try. Looking for hundred-pound bags of kitty litter is hungry work.

The restaurant was enormous, with a bare (creatively poured) cement floor replete with speed bumps, and over fifty unadorned tables scattered haphazardly about the cavernous interior. In the center of the titanic tin-roofed room there sat a jukebox the size of the Lincoln Memorial, which for the moment, thankfully, appeared to be *hors de combat*.

At the entrance to the restaurant we were greeted by no one. In fact, the entire place seemed to be abandoned. "Hello!" we cried out three or four times, to no avail. Finally, just as we were about to leave, a young man, who looked as if he'd been recently roused from a coma, approached us and said, "What do you want?"

"We'd like something to eat," I said, "if the kitchen is open."

"Of course the kitchen is open," he said grumpily. "I'm Pedro, the owner," he added self-importantly.

"Great," Lucy said, "can we see a menu?"

"Yeah, sure," the young man said. "Have a seat and I'll bring one over."

The place, as I say, was entirely devoid of customers; our choice of tables, all but infinite. So we chose the scarred four-legged wooden eating surface located furthest from the gargantuan jukebox. Several weeks later Pedro reappeared with a damp largely illegible menu which he tossed onto the table like a soggy square Frisbee.

"You can't sit here," Pedro advised us the moment we began to read. "This section is reserved."

According to Pedro, though we appeared to be the only clients within a day's walk of the restaurant, the only table not reserved for these future phantom patrons was the one directly in front of the jukebox. Dutifully, we moved over there, whereupon Pedro pushed a button or two, reanimating the Frankenstein speakers which proceeded to blast out the loudest, scratchiest most painful version of *La Bamba* ever to assault the eardrums of a human being.

"Uh, Pedro," I shouted, "isn't that a little loud?"

"Yes," he screamed over the sound of the music.

"Well, could you do us a small favor," I yelled, "and turn down the volume? It's breaking up my kidney stones."

"I'll be back in a minute to take your order," he screamed. "Want something to drink?"

"No thanks," I said. "About the music…"

"You don't want anything to drink?" he demanded in an offended tone, as if I'd just insulted his mother.

"We'd like to look over the menu before we order anything," Lucy howled politely.

"You want a beer?" Pedro roared.

"No, nothing for the moment."

"A margarita?" he shrieked.

"No thanks!"

"How about some wine?" he bellowed.

The English-language menu left a great deal (almost everything in fact) to be desired. It was limited, uninteresting, overpriced and largely incomprehensible. What in the world, for example, was an order of "*Shrunken Shrimp*"? Or a plate of "*Swedish Feetballs*"? and "*Tried Chicken*"—what was that, someone's pre-masticated leftovers? But we were so hungry we decided to order something anyway, just to tide us over until we were able to get the car running and find the kitty litter factory.

"Pedro," I told the waiter, "we'll have one order of chicken enchiladas."

"And?"

"And nothing. That's it."

"Aren't you hungry?"

"Not really," I said.

"Then what are you doing here?"

"Being tortured?" my wife suggested.

"What do you want to drink?"

"Nothing."

"*Nothing*?" Pedro was beside himself. "You have to drink something!"

"Why" I asked, "is there a city ordinance requiring people to drink with their meals?"

Twenty minutes later I observed Pedro eating a plate of what appeared to be chicken enchiladas over by the kitchen.

"Excuse me," I said, approaching his table, "are those our enchiladas?"

"Yes."

"Well, why are you eating them?"

"I'm hungry."

"But we ordered them."

"Yeah, but you said you weren't hungry," was his bizarre reply.

A little while later Pedro deposited, with the aplomb of a drunken Dingo, a plate of chicken enchiladas on our table, along with one fork, no knife and no napkin.

"Could we have another fork, a few napkins and a knife?" I asked. "We're going to share."

"You're going to share one order?" he demanded with disbelief.

"Yes."

Pedro forgot the knife and the napkin, but he did bring us another fork and we commenced to dig in. The tortillas were spectacularly stale, and the chicken so tough I was afraid that at any moment it was going to bite me back. The sauce, of which there was a great deal, was an ill-defined greenish color and smelled like a cross between pumpkin seeds and lawn fertilizer.

After drowning the entire disaster in hot sauce, we began, with the greatest reluctance, to eat. But at that precise moment the jukebox suddenly and inexplicably jumped a dozen decibels in volume, something I would not have thought possible. "Pedro," I screamed, "could you turn the music down, please?"

"No, the other customers like it loud," was his surly reply.

"But there *are* no other customers!" I pointed out.

"There will be," he claimed. "Tomorrow is a holiday. What do you want to drink?"

"Bring us the check, please."

"The check? Don't you want dessert? We have an excellent banana flambé today. It was made yesterday, but it's still warm."

"I think we'll pass on the dessert."

It was then that Lucy discovered a large bone enveloped in one of our enchiladas. Ordinarily such a discovery would not have alarmed us; after all, chickens do have bones. But this particular bone did not belong to any winged creature we could imagine—unless it was a pterodactyl.

"What's this, Pedro?" Lucy screamed, holding aloft the sizeable body part with both hands.

"That's a bone," Pedro shouted back.

"Yes, but from what kind of animal?" I asked.

"How should I know?" he replied irritably. "I'm a restaurateur, not a veterinarian."

The Two Eves

I would like to take this opportunity to publicly apologize, once again, to the entire *Yelapa* winter expatriate community, a really splendid group of people, no matter what you may have read to the contrary.

Only twice in my life have I truly felt what they call "filled with remorse". The first instance involved a *Win a Filipino Mail-Order Bride* contest I entered several years ago, an account of which I plan to publish, posthumously, in *Wedding* magazine. The second attack of undiluted regret was brought on by a story I wrote in which (to my eternal chagrin) I had the temerity to present the afore-mentioned expatriate Yelapan community in something less than a glittering light.

How much less than glittering? One troubled reader pretty much summed it up in an e-mail he sent to me shortly after the story's publication. "So, do any normal people live in Yelapa," he asked, "or are they all a bunch of raving lunatics?"

"*Raving lunatic* is a relative term," I e-mailed back.

What made me change my entire Yelapan perspective was a splendiferous Valentine's Day weekend my wife and I recently had the privilege of spending there.

We had no way of knowing it, but Valentine's Day is the absolute, undisputed pinnacle-by-default of the entire Yelapa social season. It marks the culmination of the annual croquet tournament, which is followed by the spectacular costume party and ball. It was at this pair of world-class events that Lucy and I were able to make the acquaintance of so many marvelous, talented, seemingly *normal* expatriates who make the place their winter home.

Yelapa, set inside a spectacularly beautiful little bay, has its very own river and is surrounded by lush sub-tropical mountains. And best of all, being accessible only by boat, it is blissfully free of automobiles.

Hopping off the water-taxi and onto the pristine beach, we set off at once to locate the site of the *Internationally Sanctioned Yelapa Croquet Tournament*, and promptly got lost.

After asking seven or eight people for directions, we finally managed to find the actual location just as the tournament was coming to its climactic conclusion. The little I know about croquet could probably be written on the inside of an aging hippy's hairy ear. But it seemed to me that the irregular and badly sloping field, sparsely sprinkled with grass and liberally littered with rocks, bushes and other non-scheduled impediments, must have presented quite a challenge to the contestants.

In this assumption I was not wrong: the winning score was so high it had to be computed by abacus.

After lugging ourselves back down to "town", we had some excellent fish on the beach at *Domingo's*, went home and prepared ourselves for the evening's festivities. Since we had not brought any costumes along, I decided to disguise myself as a middle-aged skinny person, while Lucy daringly donned a floral print dress.

The *Ninety-Ninth Annual Yelapa Costume Contest and Ball* was held on the beach, beneath an enormous palapa. Arriving just after seven, we were surprised to see well over two hundred people in attendance, most of them masquerading as peculiar-looking expatriates.

The remaining attendees, the ones who had dressed in real costumes in order to compete for the various cash prizes, were bursting with excitement and enthusiasm. With a liter of *raicilla* to keep us company, we settled in at a small weather-beaten table so filled with termites you could actually hear them chewing the wood. After downing several shots of my favorite firewater, and giving my favorite wife a big sloppy wet Valentine's Day kiss, I sat back and prepared to enjoy the show.

Sadly, lack of motivation prevents me from describing all of the marvelous and highly creative costumes, so I will merely mention a few of my personal favorites. The very first contestant hobbled onto the makeshift stage dragging in his wake a dozen (empty) five-gallon plastic water jugs and carrying a tall stack of tortillas, which he proceeded to graciously distribute one by one to the crowd. He called himself the "Purified Water and Tortilla Man", and was welcomed with a thunderous round of applause.

Then, by a most remarkable coincidence, we were treated to the extraordinary spectacle of, not one, but *two* "Eves". The first Eve entered stage-left carrying part of a tree with apples glued to it. The second Eve arrived five contestants later with a snake around her neck. The snake appeared to be alive (unlike the tree), but unnaturally still. Straining our eyes we attempted to determine the metabolic status of the inert serpent. Was it sleeping? Was it dead? Or had it simply been in Yelapa too long?

Then there were the "group" contestants. One consisted of an Arab sheik accompanied by his harem— three mustachioed men dressed unconvincingly as women. Another group, wearing black robes, had their faces elaborately painted in the style of the rock group *KISS*, or extras from the *Night of the Living Dead*.

Well, on and on it went, a thoroughly enjoyable and impressive show. "This is going to be tough on the judges," Lucy opined.

"Yes," I agreed, "especially the ones who are still conscious."

Just as the judges were about to announce the winners of the umpteen different categories (with less than thirty contestants this gave everyone an excellent chance of winning something), we were joined at our table by Felipo Lo Grande, my favorite painter. Felipo is a true Yelapa legend. In the previous year's costume contest, the "*Purified Water and Tortilla Man*", disguising himself as the itinerant artist, had limped away with first place!

Felipo Lo Grande is enormously talented and, rumor has it, hung like a tapir. He is also one of only three expats who actually live in Yelapa year round, a feat requiring a certain degree of intestinal fortitude. Oddly enough, the other two year-round residents have not been sighted since 1975; locals claim it is because they have made themselves nearly transparent by consuming implausible quantities of *raicilla*.

"How'd you do in the croquet tournament?" Lucy asked Felipo.

"Only fourth place," the artist replied. "I would've placed higher, but my ball got swallowed twice."

"Swallowed? Twice?"

"Yeah. Once by a goat, and once by my next door neighbor—he thought it was a Gouda cheese."

Meanwhile, the awarding of prizes process was rolling along as smoothly as a tofu meatball, until the judges called out the winner of the "*Most Creative Costume by an Individual Person Whose Birthstone Begins with the Letter M*" category.

The winner was...Eve! The Eve who had lopped off half a tree raced up to the microphone, shedding apples left and right in her excitement, to receive the envelope containing her cash prize. As she stood beaming ecstatically at the crowd, the other Eve rushed over and attempted to wrest the envelope from her grasp. "I'm Eve," she declared, "the prize is mine!"

"No, I'm Eve," the tree-cutter insisted. "I've got the apple tree!"

"You've got half a dead hibiscus bush," the other Eve accused her, "and I've got a live snake!"

"Your snake has been doped!"

"It has not."

"It has too. I demand a urine sample!"

Suppressing a yawn, I remarked to my tablemates, "I don't think snakes actually urinate."

"They must," Lucy said.

"I'm not so sure. What do you say, Felipo, have you ever seen a snake urinate?"

"Not while I was sober," the artist replied.

In the meantime an actual tug-of-war had broken out, with both Eves clinging to the cash-laden envelope for dear life. While the two women continued to struggle, an expat dressed as a box of laundry detergent approached our table and immediately began to harangue me.

"You're that writer!" the orange box spat at me. "You should be ashamed of yourself. That article you wrote about the *Debilitism Cult* was nothing but a pack of lies. Yelapa is filled with normal people, but you made it sound like there's nothing here but a bunch of foreign nut-jobs."

Tearing my gaze away from the two tussling Eves (one dressed as a dead apple tree and one wearing a catatonic snake), I looked up at the irate cardboard box and said, "Well…"

Electric Shock Man

I n the small pueblo of *San Jose De Los Malolores* everyone was busy consuming vast quantities of lard and celebrating their Saint's Day. There was a fair, of course, featuring seventy-year-old mechanical rides salvaged from the silt-strewn shores of New Jersey. The customary contingent of taco stands (two) had magically multiplied and mutated until there were now *puestos* everywhere selling greasy bacon-wrapped hot dogs, very greasy French fries, criminally greasy *huaraches* (enormous meat and lard-laden tostadas), *atole*, hot chocolate, corn on the cob smothered in cheese, and just about everything someone hoping to die fat, young and all bunged-up like a barrel of toxic sludge could desire.

For over an hour I'd been sitting on a remarkably uncomfortable iron bench watching with wonder the colorful and frenetic activity swirling all around me, and choking on the dense clouds of vaporized cooking oil which rose from the ubiquitous food stands like mini-mushroom clouds over their respective Hiroshimas.

Night had long since fallen and I was seriously considering calling it quits (after one last order of ultra-fried bananas smothered in sweet cream) when an ancient supernaturally skinny little man came to an unsteady halt before my bench and took a shaky bow. In his gnarled hands he held a small wooden box from which protruded two long wires, which were in turn attached to a pair of round metal bars about four inches long.

"*Buenas tardes*," he croaked politely. "Feliciano Suarez Luna at your service. Would you like a shock?"

"Yes," I replied, "tell me my wife is going to be on time from now on."

"Making women punctual?" he laughed. "I cannot perform miracles. But I can help to put your spiritual and emotional equilibrium back into a state of naturalized harmony."

"No kidding? How do you do that?"

"With these," he said, offering me the iron bars. "I will give you the first shock for free so that you can experience the great benefits."

"An electric shock?" I asked.

"Yes."

"Why would I want an electric shock?"

"Because, as I was saying, it will help to put your naturalized harmony back into the state of emotional equilibrium which every human being deserves."

"I see. Well, I think I'll pass on the shocks, but I would like to ask you a few questions. If you don't mind?"

I had been looking for a colorful subject for an interview for several weeks and it suddenly occurred to me that an old paper-thin man who sold electric shocks for a living was probably about as gaudy as I was going to get.

"Under normal circumstances, it would be my privilege," Feliciano declared. "But this is one of my busiest nights of the year, so..." Smiling regretfully, he left the unfinished sentence dangling in the air, like an upturned palm.

After paying for the equivalent of two shocks and a jolt, I invited the weaving watt monger to take a seat beside me.

The interview, which lasted half the night, began on the bench, continued at Feliciano's favorite taco stand and concluded at the volt vender's cantina of choice. It was at the cantina, after our fourth mescal, that Feliciano confessed to me that the "spirtiual harmonizing" line was just a sales pitch, that nearly all of his customers were men who shared two things in common: they were drunk, and they wanted to prove to their pals how macho they were.

"I charge them by the volt," Feliciano cackled confidentially. "And the drunker they are, the more volts they can take. And the more they can take, the more I make!" Feliciano burst into a long fit of raspy laughter, which ended in an equally long fit of serious choking. Before I left him listing leeward on his stool, and trading shots for shocks with the bartender, we exchanged addresses and swore solemn oaths of eternal friendship and fealty.

Not even in my most improbable fantasies did I ever imagine that six months later Feliciano would actually show up in Puerto Vallarta with his batteries fully charged and ready to do business in, of all places, my wife's shop. My first inclination was to dismiss the idea out of hand. It was too absurd. And my wife would be furious to the point of...

"Yes, Feliciano," I told my long-lost friend, "I would be honored if you could offer your services to our customers. In fact, why don't we start right away."

"With *her*?" Feliciano asked, a slight tremor in his scratchy voice.

Feliciano was referring to Mrs. Lynch, an imposing woman of great wealth and impeccable taste who had harbored serious doubts about my cerebral status quo for a number of years now. "Your husband is quite...unusual," she'd once told my wife.

"Sure, go ahead," I told him.

After taking a few moments to gather his courage, Feliciano (who might have missed a bath or two on the long bus ride north) marched bravely up to the stout woman and thrust the metal bars under her chin.

"What in God's name is this?" she cried, backing away.

"Oh, it's a special promotion we're having, Mrs. Lynch, particularly for our best repeat clients like yourself."

"A *promotion*? Where's your wife?"

"A good question, Mrs. Lynch, and one I've been asking myself repeatedly for the last twenty years. But getting back to the promotion, have you read about the spiritual and emotionally therapeutic benefits of *CMES*?"

"No," she said, eyeing Feliciano warily. "What is it?"

"It stands for *Controlled Manageable Electrical Stimulation*," I replied with clinical precision. "It's worked wonders with the lepers of Batswannaland, and I'm fairly certain it can help you, as well."

"Are you talking about electrical shocks?" she demanded.

"Yes, Mrs. Lynch, I certainly am. As they say in the sports world, no pain, no gain. Sr. Feliciano here is..."

"When is your wife coming back?" she inquired fearfully.

At the sound of his name, Feliciano began to inch forward, launching animatedly into his sales pitch, not a word of which Mrs. Lynch could understand. All she knew was that a tiny, malodorous old man holding out a pair of electrified iron bars was moving in her direction—smiling, mumbling incomprehensible gibberish and drooling sparingly onto his chin.

"Will you please control that man!" Mrs. Lynch commanded me.

"Any minute, Mrs. Lynch—I meant my wife; she'll be here any minute. But not even she will be able to beat the fabulous offer I am about to make you. With only a one thousand-peso purchase you will automatically receive a free half-hour session of *CMES*. You'll have to remove your shoes of course, and place your feet in a bucket of water. But I can assure you, the water is one hundred percent purified, utilizing a combination of reverse osmosis and ultra violet..."

But Mrs. Lynch had already fled, all but flattening the already flimsy Feliciano in her frenzy to escape.

The Final Plague

Though she stood no higher than a tall pigmy, Gertie possessed a potent voice, like a foghorn forged in Brooklyn. And she was not averse to using it, as she was now in a dementedly determined attempt to convince me that Puerto Vallarta stood on the very brink of touristic extinction due to the arrival of three successive plagues of Brian De Palma proportions.

According to Gertie the first two plagues (*The Red Tide* and *The Invasion of the Cockroaches*) had already come and gone, like a pair of poorly received B-movies. Now she stood on the sand at the foot of my terrace, wearing a powder blue shower cap and matching robe, glaring up at me with an expression of wrinkled outrage and shouting at the top of her rusty voice, "The Huns are upon us!"

Desperate for a plausible exit line, I ransacked my mind a moment before blurting out, "Speaking of Huns, that reminds me, Gertie, I'm missing my favorite show on the *History Channel*."

"What's that?" my neighbor demanded dubiously.

"Um, uh, *Attila Takes Manila*," I replied.

"What?"

"Yes, it's an, uh, historical fantasy series about what would have happened if the Huns had been sailors. Last week was, *Huns in Hawaii*, where they all become pineapple farmers. And before that it was, *On the Steppes of the Capitol*, where they invade Washington D.C. and end up taking control of Congress. Anyway, I better…"

"How can you go and watch a stupid TV program?" my obstreperous neighbor shouted. "Don't you know what's *happening*? And when is Lucy getting back? Soon, I hope— before you go running off with one of your Dutch girlfriends."

"Dutch girlfriends?"

"Yeah, those gable dancers you've been consorting with. I just pray to God you've been prophylacticking yourself properly because nowadays…"

"Gertie," I cut in soothingly, "what say we have a nice big cup of *Sleepy Time Tea*?"

"That herbal crap? No thanks. I'd rather drink wet dirt. If you're talking tea, give me *Lipton's* every time."

"All right, Gertie, *Lipton's* it is. How do you take it— with Valium or phenobarbital?"

"The little vipers are everywhere!" my neighbor shrieked.

"Now it's snakes?" I moaned.

"Worse than snakes," she vituperated. "More deadly than African bees. More revolting than banana slugs. Puerto Vallarta is about to be *buried alive* by a swarm of killer *OPCs*!"

Gertie was, I assumed, referring to those helpful, friendly well-mannered young men who stand outside their small booths inviting passersby to attend one of the fascinating time-share sales presentations so popular with foreign visitors.

"It's the third plague," she ranted on, "the worst all. The cockroaches at least we could fumigate."

"Gertie," I said reasonably, "aren't we overreacting just a little?"

"Overreacting?" Gertie repeated, stomping the sand. "Haven't you noticed how *obnoxious* they are? It's out of control. It's a crime!"

"As far as I know, Gertie, in the state of Jalisco being obnoxious is not considered a criminal offense."

"Lucky for them," she snarled, "they'd all be serving life terms."

Uneasily, I sipped my coffee and hoped for a long-distance phone call. Of course, no one ever did call me when Gertie was around. It was as if she carried with her a kind of magnetic aura capable of repelling any form of electronic communication which might interfere with her harassing me.

"Don't you think these young people have a right, just like everyone else, to earn a living?" I asked.

"Of course not," she replied. "Do you know what happened to Bernie and me last night? We were walking on the Malecon when…"

"You mean, Bernie actually left the house?" I asked in astonishment.

"Yes. He and I were walking…"

"What happened? Did they cancel *CNN*?"

"We were walking down the Malecon," Gertie rasped, "when one of those insufferable little pests had the audacity to offer me money!"

"Oh my God! What did you say?"

"I told him," my eighty-two-year-old neighbor croaked indignantly, "that I wasn't that kind of woman."

"Did this fellow happen to be holding on to a seeing-eye dog?" I asked.

"A hundred dollars he offered me, with a free breakfast thrown in for good measure! 'What do I look like,' I asked him, 'some derelict bag lady who can't afford to buy herself a decent breakfast?'"

"And what did Bernie say?"

"Not much; he was asleep."

"Asleep? I thought you were walking on the Malecon."

"We *were* walking. But then Bernie got tired, and that little blackguard offered him a chair. And you know Bernie: He hasn't turned down a chair or a doughnut in thirty years."

"So Bernie was asleep in a chair inside the booth?" I asked disbelievingly.

"Yes, leaving me to fend off the advances of this pint-sized ruffian all by myself. And then *another one* crawled out of somewhere and the two of them ganged up on me.

That's what's so scary. There's so many of them. Everywhere you look. At night, I can't sleep because I know one is going to pop his head out from under the bed and say, 'Hey lady, you had breakfast yet? Where you goin? Don you wanna take a cruise?'"

"Gertie, please, I get…"

"'Lady, where you from? Yeah? I got a cousin in New York. You like de Yankees?'"

Gertie was, I believe, attempting to imitate someone speaking English with a Mexican accent, but it came out sounding more like Woody Allen with a serious head cold.

"I'm afraid to take a shower," Gertie announced.

"A shower?" I repeated numbly.

"Yeah, just like in that movie, *Sicko*."

"You mean, *Psycho*?"

"Whatever," Gertie said. "One of these nights I'll open the shower curtain and there'll be one of them wearing a wig, saying, "Hey lady, you wanna rent a jeep?'"

"Come one, Gertie," I said reasonably, "aren't you being a little unfair? These kids are just doing their job, following orders."

"That's what the guards at *Belsen-Belsen* said," Gertie pointed out. "And they hung them anyway, at least the ones who didn't escape to New Jersey."

"All right," I yawned, "so Bernie's asleep in the chair. The kid has offered you money. And you've told him that you aren't that kind of woman. Then what happened?"

"Well," Gertie said, "then he offered me more money."

"How much?"

"Three hundred dollars. Can you imagine the impudence of that, that…anthropoid!"

"And you said?"

"I said…okay," Gertie mumbled.

"What? After all that, you went ahead and signed up anyway? What were you thinking?"

"Well," Gertie said defiantly, "things are getting so damn expensive around here. And Bernie isn't getting any younger. Last week I did some checking around, price-comparing crematoriums. Do you know what those money-grubbing vultures are charging? Fifty pesos a pound! And that's *without the urn*! The urn is optional, this crook tells me. Optional! How can the goddamn urn be optional? What am I supposed to do–carry him off in a *Ziploc*?"

Fine by Me

Even after twenty years of living in Mexico it is somehow comforting to know that I can still be beguiled and amused by the improbable peculiarities of my adopted country. A case in point: Scanning *La Prensa* recently, I came upon an article more worthy of *The National Lampoon* than of a serious daily newspaper. The dateline was *Ecatepec*, a city of two and a half million people located just north of Mexico City. Upon assuming office the mayor of said municipality had taken the seemingly bizarre step of abolishing all traffic and parking regulations.

From this moment forward, His Honor had decreed, moving and stationary vehicular violations will no longer exist!

This amazing act of jurisprudential prestidigitation struck me as being both bigheaded (in a Promethean kind of way) and highly imprudent (as in dumb). Was the mayor not opening a *Pandora's Gear Box* of potential automotive mayhem? Was he not tampering recklessly with the *Underlying Order of Things* itself?

The mayor's theory, according to the article, was that if police officers could not threaten drivers with tickets, then they couldn't shake them down for bribes, either.

"People will always speed," the philosophical mayor was quoted as saying. "They will always park illegally. But this way, at least, they won't have to pay bribes."

In most parts of Mexico the *Transito*, or traffic police, perform their duties with honesty, diligence and a high degree of whistle-tooting élan. But the area around Mexico City, I can testify from personal experience, has always been holster-deep with problematic patrolmen.

Every year my wife and I spend three to four months travelling all over the interior of Mexico searching out authentic and original folk-art to stock the shelves of our shop. In the course of these annual treasure-treks we have visited the city of Ecatepec twice in order to procure some of its highly attractive and unusual pottery. Sadly, on both occasions we encountered precisely the type of problem the mayor had been referring to, and so had vowed never to return.

Until now.

After loading up the truck with several cartons of lovely *Ecatepeckian* hand-decorated plates and bowls, we began to edge our vehicle away from the curb, only to be pulled over at once by a passing patrol car.

"Watch this," I told my wife, the sweet scent of revenge stretching my lips into a demonic grin.

"Watch what?" Lucy asked warily.

"I'm not sure yet, honey, but whatever it is, it should prove highly entertaining."

"Entertaining?" Lucy said. "Are you crazy?"

"What do you mean?"

"I mean," my wife said deliberately, "are you feeling more insane than usual?"

The policeman strutted self-importantly up to the window, leaned his head in and said imperiously, "License and registration."

"Don't you mean," I asked pleasantly, "license and registration, *please*?"

Somewhat taken aback, he said, "What? What are you talking about? Give me your license and registration. Now!"

"Why?" I asked innocently.

"You were speeding," he declared.

"Speeding?" I laughed. "I barely had time to get into traffic before you pulled me over. You'll have to come up with something better than that." Turning to Lucy I favored her with a big grin. She did not smile back.

"I do not like your attitude," the man said, his face a mask of mounting anger.

"That makes two of you," I admitted.

"What do you mean?" he asked suspiciously.

"You and my wife; neither one of you likes my attitude. Now that I think of it, I don't like it that much myself."

"Okay," the policeman said, looking increasingly confused, "I'm going to have to impound your vehicle."

This, I knew from experience, was a standard ruse utilized by corrupt traffic cops in order to frighten their unsuspecting victims into offering the proverbial bribe.

"That's nice," I said amiably.

"*That's nice?*" he repeated incredulously.

"Sure. Don't you think that's nice, honey?" I asked, turning to Lucy again.

"No," she mumbled, "I don't think that's nice."

"Sorry, I told the policeman, "she doesn't think it's nice, so I'm afraid you won't be able to impound the car."

"She has no say in the matter," the policeman sputtered, handing me an ancient moth-eaten book entitled, *State of Mexico Traffic Regulations*. "Here, read the paragraph at the bottom of the page."

I took the book and began to read the paragraph in question. Apparently, because I was a foreigner, he must have assumed that I could not read Spanish; the section he'd indicated dealt with illegal parking.

"This section deals with illegal parking," I said good-humoredly. "Now, I admit, I am prone to mental confusion on occasion, but it does seem highly improbable that I was parked illegally *and* speeding at the same time. What do you think?"

Visibly agitated, he retrieved the book, flipped through the pages and handed it back to me. "Read the paragraph at the top of the page."

"I'm sorry," I said when I had finished reading the tiny print, "I don't think this applies to me at all. As far as I can tell, this states that vehicles which have no license plates or which are demonstrably stolen, or involved in disputed traffic accidents may be impounded. But it doesn't say anything about speeding. And, of course," I added, displaying my most dazzling smile, "I was not speeding; not unless the limit here is two miles an hour."

"But you do not have a smog inspection certificate," he pointed out triumphantly. "That *is* an impoundable violation."

"There are no smog inspections in the state of Jalisco," I replied, "and this vehicle is registered in the state of Jalisco."

"But you are not in the state of Jalisco now," he said, "you are in the State of Mexico, and you must comply with the laws of this state."

"You're pulling my leg," I said, winking at my wife, who did not wink back.

(Actually, I'd said, "You're pulling my hair," which is Spanish for "You're pulling my leg.")

"I am perfectly serious," he said with feigned outrage. "I am impounding this vehicle."

"I see," I said calmly. "Hey, by the way, how's the mayor doing?"

"The mayor?" he asked guardedly.

"Yes, I was just reading about him." Reaching over the seat, I grabbed a copy of the article I'd preserved in plastic before leaving Vallarta. Handing it to him, I said, "Here, read the top two paragraphs, the ones that talk about how traffic violations no longer exist in Ecatepec."

Flummoxed beyond the hope of redemption, the policeman scanned the article, and said, "But, but, but... this only applies on weekends!"

"Nice try," I said, starting the truck and putting it into gear. "*Hasta luego.*"

The Cheap Husband

Business was kind of slow that morning. So with little to do, I allowed my mind to wander hither and yon, searching for ways to improve sales. In short order, I hit upon a scheme so brilliant it would one day win me the *Donald Trump Ego of the Year Award*. Grabbing my trusty magic marker (which had gotten me into more trouble than an unlicensed gun), I quickly lettered out a sign and hung it in the window.

The sign read: FREE GIFT COUNSELING, and the idea was to lure into the store potential shoppers who were at a loss as to what to buy for Aunt Bertha or Uncle Harry. Then, drawing upon my vast reservoirs of experience, I would aid them in selecting the most expensive gift possible.

No sooner had the ink dried on my makeshift sign than into the shop there walked my first customer. He was a balding, stoop-shouldered middle-aged man, who made a beeline for our reasonably priced collection of silver earrings. Picking a pair from the display, he approached my desk, his face a mask of indecision.

"I saw your sign in the window," he said uncertainly. "The free gift counseling…"

"Of course," I said affably, "how can I help you?"

"Well," the man said, fingering the pair of earrings, "it's my wife's birthday, and I was thinking of buying her these. What do you think?"

"What do I think of you buying a pair of five-dollar earrings for your wife's birthday?" I asked, my eyebrows arched in horror.

"Well, yes."

"My name is Gil," I said, extending my hand.

"Ernie Lyle," the man said, clasping my hand with the fervor of a dead fish.

"Listen, Ernie," I said earnestly, "I don't think a five-dollar pair of earrings is going to cut it."

"Why not?"

"Well, to answer that question adequately, I'll need some additional data. Please pull up an exquisitely hand-carved chair and take a seat."

Ernie, his mild-mannered features awash with gratitude, dutifully sat down. Reaching into a drawer I pulled out a clipboard upon which I'd affixed the instruction manual for my telephone answering machine. "Ernie, I'm going to ask you a few questions, to help me get the lay of the land, as it were. You don't mind?"

"No, of course not."

"All right," I began, perusing the instruction manual, "your wife's approximate age?"

"Oh, about fifty."

"Her height?"

"Five foot, four."

"Her weight?"

"Hard to say. It's kind of a state secret, if you know what I mean. She won't even get on the bathroom scale unless she knows I'm in the next county."

"I see," I said thoughtfully. "Well, let me ask you this: Would she look better if she weighed ten pounds more, or ten pounds less?"

"Less, definitely less!" Ernie said emphatically.

"Her favorite color?"

"Purple," he replied promptly. "Everything is purple."

"Her sexual preference?"

"Sexual...what do you mean? She's my wife!"

"Well, it's a complex world we live in today, Ernie, and there's not much left we can take for granted. So would you say, to the best of your knowledge, that your wife has lesbian tendencies?"

"Of course not. We have three children, for Christ's sake!"

"All right," I went on, staring intently at the instructions for *Recording Your Message*, "how many times would you say, on the average, you and your wife have relations each week?"

Ernie regarded me with an expression of extreme consternation.

"All right, Ernie, I'll rephrase the question: How many times a month?"

My client, his face frozen in granite, remained mulishly mum.

"Ernie," I said compassionately, "if I'm going to help you, you're going to have to open up a little here."

"All right," he said reluctantly.

"Good. So, in the last fiscal year, Ernie, how many times did you and your wife achieve coital convergence?"

"I still don't understand," Ernie grumbled, "what all this has to do with what kind of gift I should buy for her birthday."

"Everything, Ernie," I replied with professional poise. "Those five dollar earrings you're holding in your hand— you might get away with giving them to a young bride who is madly in love, and whose only desire is, well... *desire*. But in this instance, I think we will need to consult a chart generated by the *Mexican Marriage Institute* which correlates the frequency of conjugal anomalies with the amount of money a husband is required to spend on a birthday present for his wife."

"*The Mexican Marriage Institute?*"

Glancing at the instructions for *Accessing Your Messages Remotely*, I said, "In your case, Ernie—I'm assuming a score of zero to five—It would appear we are talking about a hundred-dollar bracelet. At least."

Ernie's face collapsed with shock.

"I won't go over fifty dollars," he said emphatically. "And the lack of...*relations* isn't all my fault."

"It rarely is," I said consolingly. "What's that expression—it takes a couple to copulate, or two to..."

At that moment Oscar, my favorite time-share promoter, burst into the shop on the verge of apoplexy. "Take that sign down!" he commanded me.

"Oscar, you know you're not allowed in here," I said reasonably. "I thought we had an agreement. You remain in your little niche next door, and I refrain from fumigating."

"That sign—you can't hang it there!" he shouted. "*We* give the free gifts around here. You have to *sell* them. You don't have a permit for free gifts!"

"Hold on, Oscar, you've got it all wrong. We're not giving away gifts."

"Oh no? Then what does that sign say?"

"It says," I explained patiently, "'Free Gift *Counseling*'—as in, giving a consultation."

"What does that mean?" Oscar asked suspiciously.

"I'll give you an example, Oscar. Let's say you have an accident and break your arm—no, your neck—let's say you break your neck. So you are carried away, writhing in horrible pain, to the hospital..."

"Hey, are you threatening me?" Oscar snarled.

"Not at all. And the doctor, after examining the x-rays, explains to you that your powers of locomotion are permanently impaired, and that you will never be able to chase a frightened tourist down the street again. That, Oscar, is a consultation. And that is what I am doing, giving free consultations—*not* free gifts. Giving free gifts is your department."

"Okay," Oscar said, somewhat mollified, "as long as you agree. I'll go back to my *puesto* now."

"Wonderful, Oscar, and I'll stay here and pray for your continued well-being."

"What'd you say?"

Returning my attention to Ernie, I said, "Look, Ernie, I think I have a way you can spend only fifty dollars and still avoid having your mashed potatoes poisoned."

"What's that?" he asked doubtfully.

"I'll sell you a beautiful thirty-dollar pair of earrings, and then, for only twenty dollars more, I'll throw in a dozen capsules of generic *Viagra*. What do you say?"

Ernie stared at the ground, thinking about it long and hard. Finally, he looked up and said, "I'll take the hundred-dollar bracelet."

The Gay Gringo

My manuscript, still a little rough around the edges, had to be completed in less than four weeks. But what with all the phone calls, the heat, the mosquitoes, the gas trucks, the wife, the barking dogs and the obstreperous neighbors, I was finding it almost impossible to get any work done. Then a friend offered me the loan of her *casita* in the nearby mountain town of San Pedro Del Norte. San Pedro suited me perfectly. It was small, quiet and populated with total strangers—people who, with any luck, would leave me in peace.

Upon my arrival late the following evening I found the *casita* easily enough, on the banks of a small river. The little house was crumbly but cozy: three modest rooms of weathered adobe, all of them infused with vast quantities of dust—my favorite allergen.

The dust would have to be dispensed with, but it was getting late, and I was exhausted from the grueling drive. Sneezing with enthusiasm, I lay down and went more or less to sleep.

The next morning I awoke, famished and sneezing, to the sounds of a thousand crowing roosters—music to my urbanized ears. Unused to taking care of myself (for twenty years I'd been fed, cleaned-up after and rendered generally helpless by a wife *and* a maid), the thought of preparing my own breakfast left me awash with anxiety. Blowing my nose nervously, I headed downtown to stock the larder.

El Centro, which consisted of a few tiny stores scattered around a small plaza, was a kilometer walk, all uphill. Unaccustomed to the altitude I entered asthmatically the first *tiendita* I saw and asked the owner for some milk. Would I like it warm or cold, she asked. I specified cold.

Back at the *casita* I tore open one of the huge twelve-packs of granola I'd picked up at *Sam's* on my way out of town, opened the milk carton without incident and poured a cup of cold milk over a nice handsome mound of granola. Then, sitting down at the grime-encrusted table, I shoveled a heaping tablespoon into my mouth, and immediately spat it out all over the floor. The milk had gone sour—sometime during the Portillo administration.

Starving, sneezing and wheezing I returned to the *tiendita*, where the owner handed me a rectangular carton of the "warm" milk.

"This is good?" I asked doubtfully.

"Oh yes," she said, "this kind never goes bad. Look at the expiration date: 'October 2009'."

What in God's name, I wondered briefly, could they possibly do to a liter of unrefrigerated milk which would enable it to remain "good" for more than six years? Best not to think about it, I decided.

Back in my dust-covered, sour milk-splattered kitchen I set about at once opening the eternally fresh carton of warm milk. Following the illustrated directions, I cut along a dotted line and squeezed. But nothing happened. I squeezed harder. Still nothing. I squeezed as hard as I could and the milk erupted in a white mini-geyser all over my face. Pouring what remained of the lukewarm liquid into a fresh bowl of cereal, I sat down at the indescribably dirty table and did breakfast.

My meal over, it was time to tidy up. Broom in hand I managed, with a single sweep, to fill the entire room with a noxious cloud of roiling dust. Gasping and choking, I fled for my life.

For the next hour I wandered the quaint cobble-stoned streets of San Pedro Del Norte, searching for a young woman who would take on the job of cleaning the *casita*. But all of my courteous inquiries were met with expressions of embarrassed dismay, a circumstance which puzzled me no end. Back in Vallarta there was no end to the number of people willing to work for gringos. We were considered excellent employers: kind, undemanding and generous to the point of stupidity. Returning to the *tiendita*, I detailed my dilemma to the owner, Sra. Sanchez.

Sra. Sanchez patiently explained to me that in a small conservative town like San Pedro no woman would feel comfortable working in the house of a single male, especially a foreigner.

"But I'm perfectly safe," I said. "I'm very respectful and would never attempt to take advantage of anyone."

"That may be," she replied, "but no woman in this town will work in your house if there exists even the appearance of, you know..."

For several minutes I stood there in the store, growing increasingly frantic, staring up stupidly at the *four-packs* of toilet paper stacked against the wall like a flat pyramid. I *had* to find a maid! In its current cloudy condition the casita was, for my intents and purposes, uninhabitable.

Finally, rendered dippy with desperation, I tore my gaze away from the mountain of toilet tissue and frothed the following lie: "These girls have nothing to fear from me," I declared, "I'm gay."

"You're gay?" Sra. Sanchez said, her eyes going wide.

"Yes," I said, turning pink with embarrassment.

"Well, that's, uh, interesting," she said.

Back at the casita I prepared another bowl of warm granola, which I consumed on the back porch. Then, tossing a series of small stones into the river, I attempted to gauge its true depth, just in case I decided to drown myself.

One slow-moving hour later I was startled out of my suicidal stupor by the sounds of a commotion coming from the front yard. Rushing around the house I came upon a small army of young ladies brandishing brooms and arguing with one another. "I was here first," one of them declared. "No, I was," another said. "No, I was!" a third insisted.

Wow, I thought, it looks like every girl in town wants to work for a gay gringo!

Wading into the fray I picked two of the more robust-looking candidates and set them to work. In no time the *casita* was exquisitely clean, and I was sitting down to a satisfying meal of rice, refried beans and chicken stew.

After all of the dishes had been washed and dried, I overpaid the girls, told them to come back the next day around noon and, *finally*, hauled out my laptop.

At last, all the ingredients for a prolonged and successful bout of writing were in place: a quiet dust-free house, two home-cooked meals a day, and zero distractions.

Well, not quite zero, for I soon discovered that my mendacious ploy had left in its wake several unforeseen consequences. In a matter of days every human inhabitant of San Pedro Del Norte was suffering from the delusion that an openly gay gringo was living in their rustic midst. And while no one seemed to actually disapprove, a number of people felt compelled to respond to my passage down the street with giggling (teenage girls), catcalls and whistles (teenage boys) and cries of "*Oye, mamacita!*" (drunks).

Needless to say, this verbal harassment was not altogether welcome, but at least the book was getting finished, and after twenty years of living in a foreign country I was no stranger to unwanted attention.

Then one evening, out of the blue, the Mayor showed up at my door.

"There's something I need to tell you," he said nervously.

"Of course," I said, fearing I was about to be expelled from the town. "Come on in."

We took seats at the small kitchen table and the Mayor said, "I just wanted you to know that we are delighted to have a distinguished gay writer like yourself paying us a visit. San Pedro Del Norte is a friendly town. *Very* friendly," he added with an odd emphasis.

"That's nice," I said vaguely.

"And given our close proximity to Puerto Vallarta," he added with an alarming wink, "we are very interested in promoting gay tourism."

"Of course."

"I really want to make you feel at home!" he declared with unexpected feeling.

"Uh-huh," I said, preparing to bolt for my car.

"Next week," the Mayor confided, "is our annual celebration—a very colorful and *festive* affair. And I was wondering…would you do the floral arrangements?"

"Listen, your Honor…" I began.

"No, no, no! Please, call me *Panchito*," he insisted.

Little Pancho? To even remotely qualify as "little" His Honor would have to lose about a hundred pounds.

It took another twenty minutes to convince the Mayor that I did not have the time to create floral arrangements, or be a guest at romantic candlelit dinners, or do anything but work on my book.

"I have even," I informed the amorous public servant, who had all but offered to *service me* right there on the spot, "taken a vow of chastity until my work is completed. So, thank you very much," I concluded, "and good night."

After giving His Honor the bum's rush I locked all the doors and windows and went back to work.

Several days later I was buying some bananas at the warm milk store when, to my infinite shock, two old friends, Roberto and Alba, walked in the door. After a prolonged exchange of effusive greetings, I asked (hoping desperately for an affirmative answer) if they were just passing through. No, they said, they'd been living in San Pedro for over a year.

"What are *you* doing here?" Roberto asked.

"I've borrowed a *casita* down by the river," I said with a sinking feeling. "I'm trying to finish my book."

"And Lucy?" Alba inquired anxiously. "Where is she?"

"She's up in the States," I replied, "visiting her mom."

This seemingly innocuous statement produced upon the faces of my two flustered friends expressions of profound dismay. So transparent was their reaction I could all but see the gears and crankshafts spinning and shifting inside their heads, producing in a matter of moments a single mind-numbing conclusion: "*He's* the gay gringo!"

Alba and Roberto were truly wonderful people with whom Lucy and I had been friends for many years. And, more importantly, we were the godparents of their youngest son, Alejandro, which made the four of us *compadres*—not quite family, but close enough. To their credit it took Alba and Roberto only an instant to accept what they believed to be my new "orientation" and welcome me back into the fold.

"Well…" Roberto said, after the proverbial awkward pause.

"Yes, well…" Alba agreed bravely.

"Listen," I said, "there's something I need to tell you…"

"There is no need," Roberto declared loyally, "to explain anything. You and Lucy will always be our *compadres*, no matter what you…um…I mean…"

"Alejandro is always asking after you," Alba rushed to reassure me.

"That's nice," I said, "but…"

"Rosa is going to be Confirmed next week," Roberto interrupted, and we'd like you to be the godfather. Right, Alba?"

"Yes," Alba proclaimed at once, "we'd be honored!"

"Okay, well, great," I said, "but I still need to tell you…"

"Let's go have a *raicilla*," Roberto interrupted me again. "Truly, we have something to celebrate."

The following Saturday, with serious misgivings, I put on my only long-sleeved shirt and headed up to the church to stand as godfather for Rosa's Confirmation, which turned out to be a kind of mega-event with over two hundred kids all being *Whatevered* at the same time.

(Totally out of the "Catholic Loop", I had in fact no idea what a *Confirmation* actually was; surely it bore no relation to my experience of the previous year, when I had been *Confirmed* by Alaska Airlines.)

Roberto and Alba were sitting toward the rear of the pretty church and though the place was packed solid with humanity they had managed to save me a seat on their pew. Rosa, looking more lovely than any flower, was up at the front with a multitude of other young people awaiting the start of the ceremony.

"Where did all these kids come from?" I asked my *compadres*.

"From every little *ranchito* and *pueblito* within fifty miles," Roberto explained. "They only do this once a year."

"Thank God. By the way, Roberto, I have a confession to make. The other day I kept trying to tell you…"

"Forget it," Roberto said, his tone polite but firm. "We live in a big world with lots of room for all kinds of people."

"Your choice of lifestyle is none of our business," Alba added.

"No, you don't understand. I'm not…"

Then the mass began. The priest, who I could barely hear, let alone understand, made a motion and everyone stood up. Then he muttered something, which everyone in the church repeated—except me. Then we sat down again.

This is not good, I thought. Already a one-man scandal, I wanted desperately to do nothing more than blend in with the congregation. And so the next time we were summoned to our feet, I began to improvise.

"San Francisco," I mumbled solemnly, "San Mateo, Los Angeles, San Ramon, Fresno, Sacramento, San Bernardino, San Raphael, San Diego…"

Though not the precise words spoken by the priest, they were all Spanish words, and quite a few were the names of saints, leaving me at least somewhat in the ballpark; though I did stumble occasionally, inserting inappropriately into my inane litany, "Daily City", "Stockton" and "Manhattan Beach".

But the important thing, I knew, was to appear to be participating, to keep my lips moving, and to mumble with absolute conviction.

After half an hour or so of standing up, muttering the names of cities in California and then sitting down again, I began to grow drowsy. Then I fell asleep, only to be awakened by a sharp jab in the ribs from Roberto: Everyone was standing up, except for me. Awkwardly I jumped to my feet and chanted, "San Jose, Los Gatos, Palo Alto, Marine World…"

Roberto, whose English was excellent, turned to me and mouthed the words, "*Marine World*?"

The mass proceeded apace. Stand up. Sing. Sit down. Stand up. Chant. Sit down. Stand up…This is worse than the army, I thought.

Then it was time for the Confirmation candidates to be called one by one to the altar. When Rosa's name was called, I was supposed to go and stand beside her.

"You stand to her right," Roberto advised me in a whisper.

"Will they make me drink any holy water?" I asked nervously. "If it's not purified, I'm not swallowing."

"You don't drink holy water," Alba pointed out.

Finally, Rosa's name was called by the priest. I was up and out of my pew like a roman candle, striding resolutely to the front of the crowded church. Then, standing beside Rosa, I looked expectantly at the priest, who motioned for me to approach him so he could whisper something in my ear.

"Do you have the fifty pesos for the Confirmation certificate?" he asked.

"Certificate?" I said stupidly.

"Yes, the *padrinos*, by custom, pay for the certificate. Fifty pesos," he reminded me.

"That seems kind of steep, *Padré*," I said. "How about thirty?"

"This is a House of God, not a flea market," the priest said sternly. "We do not bargain here."

"I understand, *Padré*," I said reasonably. "So, would you take forty?"

The Wrong Stuff

Working in the shop where my own books are sold has its disadvantages. But it can also be a source of great gratification: all of the kind people for example who after reading a book return to personally inform me how much they enjoyed it, how it made them laugh, how it brightened their day. Cynical though I may be, I would never stoop so low as to denigrate day-brighteners—especially when I can count myself among their shimmering number.

Then there are the somewhat less gratifying visits from fans who come to tell me what a "great writer" I am. Frankly, I find this type of misguided adulation embarrassing in the extreme. As I sit behind the desk of my wife's shop (praying to be fired) I do enjoy hearing a little praise now and then. I am, after all, somewhat human. But calling me "great" merely serves to remind me that I am not.

Worst of all are the "literary" visits. The other evening a severe-looking woman, who bore a frightening resemblance to my high school English teacher, stepped briskly through the door and up to my desk, clutching a copy of *Refried Brains*.

"Do you," she asked in a no-nonsense voice, "know the man who wrote this book?"

My English teacher had given me several Ds, once because I turned in a book report on *Lust For Life*. Miss Staples (yes, that was actually her name) was unfamiliar with the book and thought it, judging from the title, excessively risqué for our impressionable young minds. Unfortunately for her, she made the mistake of informing me of this fact in front of the entire class. Had she handled the matter more discreetly I am certain my response would have been more tactful as well.

"Miss Staples," I said, "this book is not about fornication, it's about the famous Dutch painter, Vincent Van Gough—you know, the one who cut off his ear? There's no sex in it whatsoever. No one even gets naked."

"Nonetheless," she sneered back at me, "I find it inappropriate and will not accept your report."

"Miss Staples," I said, unleashing a chain of events which culminated in yet another visit to the principal's office, "that's the dumbest thing I've ever heard in my life."

Meanwhile, back at the shop, to Miss Staples' doppelganger I replied with reluctance, "Yes, as a matter of fact, I wrote it."

"I read it," she said, a malicious gleam in her eye.

"Well," I asked after a disquieting pause, "did you enjoy it?"

"Yes," she replied, "but I wanted to ask you something: Is everything in it true?"

"Well," I admitted, "pretty much."

"Then you," she declared with professional detachment, "are a very sick man."

This remarkable reproach, delivered in the most matter-of-fact manner, left me all but mute. Several shoppers who were scattered about the store turned as one to see how I would respond.

"You should meet my high school English teacher," I finally said. "She once told me more or less the same thing. Of course, she's been dead for twenty years, which, uh, might make meeting her somewhat difficult…but, uh, you know…Have a nice day."

Several weeks later a young man with the over-eager manner of a giant puppy entered the shop and said, "My name is Omar. I really love your book."

Just to be polite I asked him which part he liked the best.

"Well, I really liked the cover," he said. "You know, I'm a writer, too!" he added energetically.

"Oh, what a coincidence," I muttered.

"Yes," he replied brightly, "and I was wondering if you could give me some advice."

"Sure," I wanted to say, "go home and take a cold shower."

"Of course," I said, "but if any customers come in, I'll have to attend them."

"Oh sure, I understand, no *problema*," he said all in a rush. "So, I've been working on this novel for two years now and I'm getting to the point where I have to make some important decisions."

"Decisions?"

"Yeah, but maybe I should tell you what it's about first."

"Oh, I don't think that's really necessary," I began, "maybe you should…"

I was going to say, "Maybe you should move to Bora Bora and take up basket-weaving," but he was already skimming along full-speed ahead.

"It's about my life," he announced, shocking me nearly senseless.

"No way!"

"Yes. My life has been pretty unique, because I was born here in Mexico, but then I went to live in the United States."

"That's, uh, pretty unusual, Omar."

"So I have so much, you know, material, that I'm thinking maybe it should be two, or even three books."

"A trilogy. Why not? You could be the next Tolkien."

"Who?"

"Never mind."

"The first book could end with junior high school," Omar enthused. "The second book could be about high school. And then the third book— that would be the climax—would be about working as a waiter at *Daiquiri Don's*—that's before I moved to Chicago," he added, just to make sure I was getting the full picture.

Where in the world are the clients tonight? I wondered desperately. Did Bush declare war on California again? Someone…please…help!

"So, I guess, where you come in," Omar went on, "is I was thinking that you could look at what I've finished so far, and maybe tell me, you know, what you think?"

"Sure, Omar, I'd love to." At this point I would've agreed to a re-circumcision, if only it would have hastened his departure. "Do you have it with you?"

"Um, no," he said, "it's at home."

"How many pages are there?"

"Finished?"

"Whatever."

"Twenty-nine. The last few months it's been going kind of slow," Omar confessed. "Because of the *Psychozac*® I'm taking—that's my medication."

Quickly I ran the numbers through my head. There were a total of 730 days in two years, which meant that Omar had been averaging almost four one-hundredths of a page per day. At that rate, if the novel were a short one—say, two hundred pages—it would only take him another fourteen years to complete.

"I see," I said, fingering the box-cutter in my pocket. "So when can I see the manuscript?"

"Um, well," Omar said sheepishly, "you see, I have to borrow a computer from someone, because everything is written by hand, and it's kind of disorganized and stuff."

"No page numbers?" I asked.

"Oh no, it's got page numbers," Omar assured me, "but it's kind of hard to read. So first I have to borrow a computer. Then I need to have someone show me how to use it. Then…"

"Time out!" I shouted, forming a "T" with my hands. "Omar, I think our discussion may be a bit premature. Perhaps, once you're further along with the project, we could…"

"It has a title," Omar broke in hopefully.

"Oh?"

Omar, like an anxious dog hoping for a pat on the head, laid the title at my feet: "*Waiting on Cables*".

"*Cables*? I thought you were a waiter, Omar."

"Yes, but I also worked for the telephone company," he explained excitedly. "You see the connection? People who are waiting for their phone lines, and people who are waiting for their food."

"Yes, Omar, it's all too clear."

"You know how in those thrillers they go back and forth?" Omar went on. "One chapter follows the protagonist. And then the next chapter follows the anti-tagonist. So that's what I'm thinking of doing—going back and forth. First, I'm working in the restaurant. Then, I'm installing telephones. Then, I'm back at the restaurant. Keep the reader off-balance. Create tension. Back and forth. Tables and cables. What do you think?"

"Omar," I said with compassion, "I think you should seriously consider doubling-up on the *Psychozac®*."

A Fridge Under Troubled Waters

People who do not know any better imagine that living on the beach in a paradisiacal place like Puerto Vallarta must perforce be a totally idyllic experience. It is not. There are in fact a substantial number of drawbacks. Among these, the most troubling has to do with the way in which the damp salt-laden air eats the heart out of all things metal. Stereos, televisions, fax machines, battery-powered vibrators—none of these delicate electronic devices has a prayer of surviving more than a few years under these perniciously corrosive conditions.

Not that we gave in easily to this discouraging process; countless trips were made to highly qualified experts, who would carefully clean the various electronic innards time and time again, until the oxidation had gone too far and there was no longer anything left to clean. Mauricio, our favorite technician, was an unusually serious man who seemed to take each losing battle personally. On one occasion, peering into the malfunctioning bowels of our Sony Trinatron he had actually groaned aloud, as if in Existential pain.

"Nothing lasts," he muttered, shaking his head dejectedly.

"The transience of existence," I sighed in agreement. "The Buddhists say that…"

"I meant, nothing electronic lasts in this lousy, mother-raping, humid salty climate," he spat with disgust.

"Oh."

"Then they blame me, as if it's my fault," he complained.

"I never blame you, Mauricio."

"That's because you're a gringo," he declared, meaning the *Divine Source of All Things* only knew what.

Our refrigerator, made of somewhat sturdier stuff, had done gallant battle against the aforementioned corrosive elements for thirteen long years. But inevitably the salt had won the war as the old gal, rotting from the inside out, finally shuddered one day to a gurgling gasping halt. There was, according to Mauricio (truly, a *Man For All Appliances*) no alternative but to buy a new one, a prospect I did not relish at all.

Since we were going to be passing through Guadalajara anyway, we decided to make the purchase there, hoping to find in that sprawling metropolis a greater variety, as well as a better price. And so it was that I found myself one fine October morning in the very heart of downtown Guadalajara, standing beside my wife as she studied the list of nineteen major appliance stores she had compiled the night before.

"So, honey," I asked, my voice quavering with repressed fear, "how do we decide which stores to visit?"

In her no-nonsense General McArthur mode, Lucy replied crisply, "What's to decide? We visit them all."

Perhaps I should pause to mention that my wife is internationally known as the Mohammed Ali of Comparison Shoppers; her eventual election to the *Shoppers Hall of Fame*, a foregone conclusion. When Lucy is shopping, she is able to draw upon vast internal reservoirs which few women (and no men) could ever hope to match. I had, in preparation for the day's ordeal, consumed three vials of ginseng extract as well as an entire quart of liquid "Protein Power", knowing all the while that nothing short of multiple goat gland injections could bring me even close to matching Lucy's superhuman level of fridge-finding fortitude.

In our third store of the day we found what would ultimately be our icebox of choice, a 19.6-cubic-foot behemoth, tastefully tinted a pale creamy yellow. It was frost-free, energy-efficient, internally buttressed with sturdy attractive shelving and blessed with an outsized freezer compartment. The shelves on the door, featuring multi built-in butter compartments, were a joy to behold. Its twin state-of-the-art produce bins were ergonomically endowed with *individual* temperature controls. And, best of all, it was *on sale.*

"Well, this looks like the one," I said hopefully, encouraged by the expression of freonic bliss on my wife's beaming face.

"Maybe," she said noncommittally, "and maybe not."

Fourteen stores later, haggard with fatigue, I decided to plead for mercy. "You know, honey," I said cautiously, "men just aren't built for this kind of thing. God made males to be swift and strong so they could run down defenseless deer, kill lions with their bare hands and…"

"And come in less than fifteen seconds?" Lucy suggested.

"No, no, honey, I'm talking about hunting swift and elusive prey, an exclusively male activity."

"Well, then hunting down refrigerators should be a piece of cake for you," Lucy said sweetly. "*They* stand still."

"That's not the point," I whined with conviction. "Women are built for endurance, the prolonged agony of childbirth, that kind of thing; while we men are born to run."

"I agree," Lucy said. "So run over to the counter and see if you can hunt down a salesperson. I'll be checking out that yellow *GE* with the automatic icemaker."

Six hours after beginning our quest, we were back in store number three, standing in awe before the same 60,000-cubic kilometer monster, with an anxious saleslady at our side, order form in hand. "So, is this it?" I asked impatiently.

"Probably," my wife said, "but you're making me nervous. Why don't you take a walk around the block. I want to be alone for a while with the refrigerator."

She's insane, I decided, but all I said was, "Of course, honey, I understand."

The fridge arrived at our decaying beach house several days after we did. Once removed from its Godzilla-sized box, it did indeed look magnificent standing there tall and proud in the heart of the kitchen.

"Okay," I said, delighted to finally see my wife on the verge of cooking me a meal again. "Let's plug that baby in!"

"We can't. They said we have to wait for the gas to settle down first."

"And how long does that take?"

"Twenty-four hours."

"You gotta be kidding."

Twenty-four hours later, as the entire state of Jalisco waited with bated breath, I was permitted to plug in the refrigerator. "All right," I cried with glee, "let's put some perishable provender in that puppy."

"Not so fast," Lucy said. "We have to wait eight more hours before putting anything inside."

"Says who?"

"Says the instruction manual."

"I'm sure they didn't mean that literally, honey."

"We're going by the book," Lucy said with finality, "and that's that."

The next morning I awoke, starving for a home-cooked breakfast, to find my wife sitting in front of the fridge staring at it lovingly, the way she used to look at me before we were married. The fridge, humming quietly like a far-off ocean liner, stared cheerfully back.

"Isn't it beautiful?" she asked dreamily.

"Yes, it's beautiful," I agreed, "and so are you. What's for breakfast?"

The next four days passed in frost-free, energy-efficient bliss. We bought food. We cooked it. We ate it. We placed the leftovers reverently on the sturdy yet attractive shelves. We were, in a word, content.

On the morning of the fifth day, however, we suffered, refrigerator-wise, something of a setback. After staying up all night listening to the radio blather on about a "Category Five" hurricane which might or might not hit Vallarta, we decided to grab a few valuables and forthwith vacate the premises. Ten minutes later a forty foot wave rushed ashore, blasting our beachfront abode and everything in it to smithereens.

Among the casualties of this untoward event, the new fridge ranked high on the list. It was gone, lost without a trace.

Or so we thought.

Almost a week later, scavenging under the nearby *Bridge of Shrimp*, I found the door to the freezer compartment. At my wife's insistence, I wrapped the door, as well as a rather soggy "Eight-Year Guaranty," in cardboard and mailed it to the Maytag company headquarters, accompanied by a note in which I demanded that they replace this obviously defective piece of merchandise; or at the very least, utilizing the freezer door as a template, clone a replacement.

I am still waiting for a reply.

Every Shroud Has a Silver Lining

I n 1980 I moved to Santa Monica, California, in an ill-omened, ill-advised, ill-starred attempt at becoming a screen writer. On the verge of insolvency, I rented a small seedy studio apartment in a building which had never known better days and set to work establishing a rigid routine: six hours of writing, followed by lunch, followed by a walk along the Venice Boardwalk, where I hoped to meet the girl of my dreams.

It did not take me long (one day) to discover that a young man with a crumby car, no job and very little money stood no chance whatsoever of connecting with one of the beautiful young women who seemed to sprout spontaneously from the fertile LA asphalt, like dandelions on a lawn.

Most of these sweet-and-sour young things called themselves "model-actresses", and were surprisingly approachable, at least at first. Constantly on the lookout for a man who could help their careers, and/or substantially raise their standard of living, they could not afford to ratchet their turned-up noses even a millimeter higher until they knew who exactly they were talking to.

And they were not at all shy when it came to finding out. Within minutes of striking up a "casual" conversation with one of these *robo-babes*, she would be grilling me like a homicide detective. What kind of car did I drive? Where did I live? And, most important of all, was I in a position to help her career? My honest replies (remember, I'd only been in

LA a few days) were greeted with polite but firm dismissals. One particularly scrumptious little gumdrop even shook my hand and said, "Good luck," before turning her outstanding behind on me and stalking sensuously away.

On my third night in the new apartment I was awakened at one am by the telephone, which had only been installed that morning.

"Whoever this is..." I began to say, but was interrupted by a man's voice declaring:

"I'm going to kill myself!"

Assuming it was a crank call, I said with irritation, "Congratulations!" and hung up.

The next morning, just as I was getting into a good writing groove, the phone rang again. It was a woman this time, and incredibly enough the first words out of her mouth were, "I'm going to kill myself!"

Absolutely certain that I was the victim of some sick practical joke, I replied, "That's nice."

"That's nice?" she shrieked into the phone. "That's all you can say? Aren't you supposed to talk people *out of* committing suicide? Isn't that your job? I need help. I'm desperate! My husband..."

"Listen, lady," I broke in, "I don't know if you think you're being funny, or you're crazy, or what, and frankly dear, I don't give a damn!" Already, Hollywood was getting to me.

"But..."

Slamming down the receiver I went back to work, but almost at once a highly unpleasant thought began to gnaw at the edges of my consciousness. Finally, I picked up the phone and dialed information. "Do you have a listing for a *Suicide Prevention Hotline*?" I asked. After the regulation, "One moment please," she came back on the line and recited to me my own phone number!

Oh my God! I thought, I've just sent two desperate people to their doom! Highly distressed myself now, I began to pray that they would call back and give me a chance to redeem myself. But they never did.

So I contacted the phone company and outlined the basic situation.

"Yes," a disinterested woman informed me, "these little mistakes happen all the time."

"Little mistakes!" I shouted. "Don't you understand? My phone number is listed as the *Suicide Prevention Hotline*! Can't you do something?"

In a bored voice the woman explained that my only option was to change my number, which would cost thirty dollars, and take about a week. "Fine, just do it!" I told her.

An hour later my phone rang again. "Is this the *Suicide Hotline*?" a man asked nervously.

"Well…um…what seems to be the matter?"

"My liver is shot," the man declared. "The doctor says if I have one more drink I'm going to die."

"So," I said, "don't drink."

"I've got a glass of bourbon sitting right in front of me," he announced, "and I'm going to drink it right now."

"Whoa, hold on, take it easy," I said, determined to make up for my earlier callous behavior. "Just tell me one thing: Why are you going to take a drink? Why is drinking that bourbon more important than life itself?"

"It's my career," the man whined. "I've been trying to sell a screen play for ten years and no one wants it. I can't stand the rejection any more. I'd rather die."

Just what I needed to hear.

For the next hour I did my best to bolster the poor fellow's ego. I talked about Franz Kafka and how he died without ever having published a single word. I talked about James Joyce and how it took him over twelve years to find a publisher for what was probably the greatest novel ever written. I talked my heart out and when I was done, the distraught writer said, "You know, you're right. I just have to keep on going. I'm throwing this glass away. Thanks. You've saved my life!"

Well, I thought with some satisfaction, at least now I'm batting one for three—right up there with Mickey Mantle.

Over the next several days I took fourteen calls. Oddly enough, I turned out to have a real knack for this suicide prevention business. More often than not the call ended with a promise from my "patient" to give life another chance.

But all of those tense morbid conversations were beginning to take their toll. I couldn't work. I couldn't sleep. I found myself mentally measuring the heights of ceiling fixtures, studying the warning labels on containers of toxic toilet cleansers and staring at vertiginously narrow window ledges.

I finally decided to unplug the phone. But before I could, it rang one more time.

"Is this the *Suicide Hotline*?" a woman asked.

"Yeah, what is it?" I said morosely.

"I'm going to shoot myself."

"You have a gun?" I asked in a bored voice.

"Yes. I bought it for protection."

"That was smart."

"It's loaded and I'm holding it in my hand," she warned me.

"Why do you want to kill yourself?" I yawned.

"You'll probably think I'm crazy," she said unnecessarily, "because in many ways I have everything to live for. I'm young and beautiful, and I have a successful modeling career. But I just can't seem to meet a decent man. It's hopeless. They're all a bunch of creeps. I want to die!"

Young? I thought to myself. Beautiful? Modeling career?

"Maybe the problem," I said, wide awake now, "is the kind of man you're attracted to. It sounds like you could have your pick. Maybe you're simply picking wrong."

"I don't know," she said forlornly. "I just want someone who's reasonably good looking, sensitive and intelligent. Someone nice," she added and began to cry.

"Listen," I said, "that gun—you've got to get rid of it. You're just experiencing a momentary despair. You'll get over it. But having that gun around is dangerous."

"Okay," she sniffled, "I'll get rid of it. But how? I can't just throw it in the garbage disposal."

"I'll take it off your hands," I said helpfully. "The sooner the better."

"All right," she said. "How can we…"

"You know *Sam's Café* on the Venice Boardwalk?"

"Yes?"

"Could you meet me there in an hour?"

"Yes, yes. Oh, thank you!" she sighed gratefully. "But how will I know you?"

"That's easy," I said, smiling slyly at myself in the cracked mirror, "just look for a nice, sensitive, intelligent, reasonably good-looking guy. And if you don't see him, I'll be wearing a red shirt."

Red Alert

Anyone who spends more than fifteen seconds in our fair city soon becomes aware of what are commonly referred to as OPCs. OPCs are the remarkably helpful young men and women one sees stationed all over town in those cute little booths. Their principle function (aside from being helpful) is to encourage visitors to attend time-share presentations.

Several years ago my wife and I were blessed with the birth of a lovely little OPC booth right next to her store. So delighted were we with this marvelous turn of events that for several days afterwards we seriously considered moving to Bangladesh.

Aside from taking up permanent residence in Bangladesh, my foremost goal in life, as everyone now knows, is to be fired from my job. But my wife, whose only faults are an excess of patience and understanding, has so far refused to cooperate.

Then, the other morning, as I sat behind my desk staring at our incomparable collection of Oaxacan wooden animals, I was seized by a brilliant idea—a way to kill two roaches with one shoe—a way to finally get myself fired, while at the same time performing a valuable community service.

The concept was dazzling in its simplicity: I would devise a color-coded "Tourist Alert System" (based upon the American model) and place the appropriately colored sign in the window of the shop. Four colors would be sufficient, I decided: LOW PINK (relatively innocuous), HIGH YELLOW (somewhat obnoxious), VERY HIGH ORANGE (insufferable) and EXTREME RED (grab a cab).

The next day, after opening the shop, I stepped out onto the sidewalk in order to assess the current *threat level*. The supernaturally friendly OPCs who worked the booth next door were rotated on a daily basis. On this typically pristine Vallarta morning, it was Betty's turn. I liked Betty; she was particularly amiable and every time she called out to passing tourists, "Hi, are you going to breakfast?" I broke out in goose bumps. The tourists, I had observed, were equally delighted to know that a total stranger was apparently so concerned with their nutritional well-being. Betty, in my expert opinion, rated a YELLOW.

I affixed the sign, boldly lettered with the words, "TODAY'S THREAT LEVEL: HIGH YELLOW", on the storefront window and sat down to have my morning coffee. No sooner had the cup touched my lips than into the shop there rushed Mrs. Barrett, a nervous near-sighted woman in her late fifties.

"Is there a terror alert in Puerto Vallarta?" she demanded breathlessly. "Should I go back to the hotel?"

"No, no, Mrs. Barrett," I said reassuringly. "The last thing we want is to disrupt your vacation. In fact, we urge you to go normally about your shopping, as if nothing had happened. Just remain tense, and try to relax. And don't forget to keep your eyes and ears open."

"Open for what?" she asked apprehensively.

"For unusually annoying behavior," I replied. "But whatever you do, don't fall prey to panic. We have taken every precaution to insure that your vacation is a tranquil one."

"What the hell are you talking about?" she demanded.

"You see, Mrs. Barrett," I patiently explained, "this is just the kind of thing we're trying to avoid. We want you to be prepared, but not paranoid. Alert, but not anxious. Suspicious, but not mistrustful. By the way, have you heard about our duct tape and rubber glove sale? Two for one, with every purchase over a thousand dollars."

"You've been drinking that *raicilla* again," Mrs. Barrett said, narrowing her eyes. "Where's your wife?"

"She's at the gym right now. I'll give you her cell number. You can probably catch her between the treadmill and the weight machines, if you hurry."

"I will. Can I use your phone?" she asked.

"No, I'm sorry, Mrs. Barrett, we've been requested by the *Department of Homeland Insecurity* to keep our lines of communication closed at all times."

After she'd left (with an exquisite gallery-quality woven wool rug under her arm), I ambled outside where I noticed at once that Betty had been joined by Oscar, who was somewhat lacking in the finesse department. "Hey, come back here!" Oscar was shouting at a pair of elderly tourists hobbling by on canes. "Where are you going? I'm *talking* to you!"

Uh-oh, I thought, time to change the threat level. Replacing the yellow sign with an orange one, I returned to my desk and took out an unfinished drawing I'd been sketching of a helpful young man with a wooden stake protruding from his chest.

Before long a young couple from Ontario burst into the shop and began talking at the same time in excited voices. "What does that sign mean?" the husband asked. "Has something happened?"

"What's the best price you can give me for that metal cat?" the woman inquired.

To the husband I said, "No, nothing has happened." And to his wife I explained, "The best price is the one on the sticker."

"But then, what does that sign mean?" the man asked.

"But we're Canadians," the woman said.

Patiently, I explained to the husband the ins and outs of my tourist alert system, which left the man speechless with amazement. Then, to his wife I said, "That's nice. Some of my best friends are Canadian."

"But we have a terrible exchange rate," the woman said. "That metal cat would cost us almost twenty Canadian dollars!"

"I know," I said sadly, "it's a real shame. Fortunately for you, you're not Japanese or Italian."

"What?"

"Well, that same cat would cost a Japanese person $1,800 yen, and an Italian person $22,500 lira. Just thank your lucky maple leaves that you were born in Canada!"

At this point the man grabbed his wife's arm, said, "This fellow is crazy; let's get out of here," and dragged his spouse bodily from the shop.

Later that morning, just after I had sold three uniquely beautiful silver bracelets at our great everyday low prices, my wife strode into the shop, still in her gym clothes.

"Hi, honey," I said, favoring my boss with a broad grin.

For some reason, the expression on her lovely face was sort of angry. In fact, it was downright terrifying. Uh-oh, I thought grimly, it's time for *Code Red*.

Lopsided Jaguars

Every year my wife and I spend the summer coaxing our old truck up and down the rutted roads of rural Mexico, losing countless mufflers in the process, as we search for original pieces of quality folk-art to adorn the walls of our small shop in Puerto Vallarta.

We love these summer excursions for many reasons, but most of all we love visiting with the hundreds of artisans we have come to know and admire, the folk-artists who, in my modest opinion, produce the world's most varied and beautiful *Arte Popular*.

Some of these artisans we have known as long as twenty years. We have watched them refine their craft, struggle to make a living, get married, raise families, grow old and, in several cases, become completely dysfunctional.

Among this last small select group, two individuals stand out from all the rest: Maximino Hidalgo Juarez and his son, who everyone (for reasons unexplained) calls "El Pollo".

Maximino and *The Chicken* live in a small, remote dusty town in the lowlands of Oaxaca, surrounded by a choppy sea of dry tortured hills known as *La Tierra Caliente*. When we first met them almost twenty years ago, Maximino was forty-eight years old and *The Chicken*, a spry springy twenty-three. Immensely talented, their specialty was taking old round copper floats (once used in toilet tanks) and ingeniously fashioning them into stylized jaguar masks.

Once the masks were formed and painted, the men dipped them into a tub filled with acid, giving the masks an instant "antique" patina.

On our first visit to his humble home we were completely taken with Maximino's amazing artistry. For more than two hours we sat entranced in his tiny backyard watching him work, looking on as he molded and soldered the stylized jaguar face, and then as he painted it, and set it down to dry in the smoldering sun.

Lucy and I could have watched Maximino work forever, had he not abruptly dipped the now-dry mask into a washtub filled with acid. At this point, seeing the small greenish clouds of dense vapor billowing up from the interior of the tub, we began to grow a little anxious.

Then, as our eyes, noses and throats confirmed what our brains had already surmised (that we were sitting in the midst of a mini-*Three Mile Island*), we leapt to our feet and power-walked out of there, calling back over our shoulders (for the sake of politeness): "We're thirsty. We're getting some *refrescos*. Want one?"

Maximino, squatting beside the tub, his head all but engulfed in the noxious clouds, grunted noncommittally as he continued to stare from close range down at his work-in-progress, his own face a mask of sun-dried concentration. "Timing the acid bath," he'd told us, "is kind of tricky."

Down the street at the local *tiendita*, Lucy and I stood sipping on our sodas.

"I can't believe he's sitting there breathing that stuff in," she said.

"Me, neither. I mean, if that acid instantly antiques paint, think what it does to your lungs!"

"Do you think it's affecting his brain?" Lucy asked with concern.

Before I could venture an opinion, we were joined by *The Chicken*, who we invited to a *refresco*.

"I never drink *refrescos*," he demurred, "they're bad for my teeth. But I wouldn't mind a mescal," he added hopefully.

The owner of the *tiendita*, a tiny white-haired woman, somehow managed to muscle a large unlabeled glass jug onto the high wooden counter, serving *The Chicken* a double shot.

"*Salud!*" he said, draining the glass, and I wondered, not for the last time, how and why he had come to be called *The Chicken*.

For eleven years we continued to do business with Maximino and his son. On our way south we stopped off and left them a deposit; then, on the way home, we picked up our order. And everything was fine.

But the twelfth year, when we attempted to entice Maximino into *sending us* our masks (a task which, in degree of difficulty, came to resemble the building of a trans-oceanic canal), things stopped being fine. Forever.

Once again we found ourselves standing in the cramped confines of Maximino's sweltering postage stamp backyard.

"My father is a little under the weather," *The Chicken*, who looked much the worse for wear himself, informed us.

"So what happened to our masks?" I asked.

"We have some," he hurried to say. "We have some finished."

"Listen, *Pollo*," I said, forcing myself to remain calm, "we're already a year late here, and from my point of view..."

"I understand, I understand," *El Pollo* said. "Hey! You want some mescal? Let's have some mescal. For old time's sake."

Before I could reply to this dubious proposition, Maximino himself entered stage left carrying a large *costal* made lumpy by its mysterious contents.

"Papi," the Pollo told his father triumphantly, "our old friend Don Gilberto has just invited us all to a bottle of mescal!"

"Fuck the mescal!" Maximino rumbled, withdrawing from the sack a jaguar mask and holding it up for my edification. The jaguar, I noticed at once, had both ears on the same side of its lopsided head.

"Maximino," I said uneasily, "this mask is very nice, but...the ears...look at the ears!"

"The hell with the mother-raping ears!" he growled.

Bulldozing flat my better judgment, I handed *El Pollo* fifty pesos to buy a bottle of mescal. Then I began to remove the masks from the long cotton sack and pass them, one by one, forlornly along to Lucy.

The masks were like nothing we had ever seen. Many were deformed or missing key anatomical features. Or, if they were more or less intact, they were painted in grotesquely inappropriate colors (hot pink, mostly, with splashes of lime-green). A few of them appeared to have been run over by farm vehicles.

"It must be a joke," I said in English.

"Masks are good," Maximino said with difficulty, his eyes glazed with thirty years of respired fumes.

"Each mask is one of a kind," *El Pollo*, returning with the mescal, pointed out proudly.

"Thank God," Lucy muttered.

The Chicken, a propos of nothing said, "I lived in Los Angles for four months." Then, after making the sign of the cross three times in rapid succession, he poured everyone a drink.

The mescal was *Zippo*-friendly, so strong I was surprised it did not spontaneously combust right there in my chipped glass. The taste was unspeakable, like sipping from a can of liquid drain de-clogger. But *The Chicken*, with Maximino looking on (sort of), downed it merrily, shot after tongue-blistering shot.

"You better take it easy, *Chicken*," I cautioned him, "you're gulping it down like it was lemonade on a hot day."

"Yes," he replied sagely, "and every day is a hot day in *La Tierra Caliente*."

Numbered Rages

The day we moved into our new Vallarta house Lucy and I began to receive improbable quantities of phone calls from digitally challenged individuals wishing to speak to people we had never heard of. There were calls from men wanting to speak to Maria, women hoping to reach Alonzo, men and women intent on ordering flowers, buying meat, seeking sexual favors and complaining about overcharges on their credit cards.

At first the sheer absurdity of it all left us laughing and rolling our eyeballs skyward in bemused disbelief. But the cheery smiles and giggles petered out in short order, leaving in their place any number of scowls and a good deal of grumbling.

Of all the wrong numbers the ones which irked me the most were from North Americans calling in the wee hours of the morning in the hopes of procuring a taxi. Every now and then one of them would actually have the audacity to *argue* with me, insisting that they were right and I was mistaken—as if somehow it had slipped my mind that I was operating a taxi service!

"What's with these people?" I complained to my drowsy wife. "Why can't they dial a simple phone number? Were they lobotomized at the border? Or are they…"

"Go back to bed," my wife suggested.

Late one night about a week later, a particularly insistent fellow drove me right past the point of no return, allowing the Devil to slip in and take temporary control of my larynx. "Okay, *amigo*," I said, "I'll be there in five minutes. Just wait outside."

"But it's raining," he complained.

"So?" I sneered. "Is that my problem? What's the matter—you gonna melt or something?"

As I lay in bed struggling to re-lose consciousness, Lucy said, "That wasn't very nice."

"Neither was waking me up," I growled.

The next morning as I sat at the laptop struggling with Chapter LXXXVIII of my never-ending novel, the phone rang yet again, and like a fool I picked it up. The man at the other end wanted to know if we had sirloin steaks today and, if so, how much a kilo were they.

"No sirloins," I replied in my best busy-butcher's voice, "but we are having a special today on pork ribs, ground beef, T-Bones, pork chops and rib-eye. Seventy percent off."

"*Seventy percent off?*"

"*Sí, Señor*, but you better get your ass down here fast; there's a line halfway round the block. No," I shouted to an imaginary client, "only ten kilos per customer!"

"Okay, okay," the man said excitedly, "reserve me ten kilos of pork ribs. I'll be there in an hour."

"No can do," I replied. "Fist come, fist serve. Hey you!" I yelled off-phone again, "keep your filthy hands off my Polish sausage!"

Later that day the phone rang again, and this time I rushed to pick it up, literally grabbing it out of Lucy's hands. A man was on the line, wanting to talk to Leticia.

"Who is this?" I asked impatiently.

"This is her husband," he replied proprietarily.

"One minute," I said. Holding the receiver several feet from my mouth, I shouted the following Spanish phrases at our cat: "There's a man on the phone. He says he's your husband. You want to talk to him?"

"Meow," the cat replied.

"I thought you were laying off the peyote this week," Lucy remarked wryly.

"She can't come to the phone right now," I said into the mouthpiece. "She's busy.".

"She's *busy*?" the man repeated in disbelief. "Who are you? And what the hell are you doing in my house?"

"I'm a friend; a *very good* friend," I replied calmly. "And what I'm doing in your house is showing your wife what a normal-sized penis looks like. Have a nice day."

The moment I hung up the phone my face broke into a broad grin, but Lucy was not amused. "What are you doing?" she cried. "What if he believes you? He might do something terrible."

"You're right, I hadn't thought of that," I said contritely. "If he calls back, tell him it was all a misunderstanding."

As the days passed I began to look forward to the wrong numbers. I tried to explain why (with mixed results) to my wife. "I'm merely making a negative into a positive," I told her over dinner. "Taking something that normally gets me upset, and instead converting it into a source of entertainment."

"That's all well and good," Lucy said, "but what about the poor people on the other end?"

"What about them?"

"Haven't you noticed," she pointed out, "that, except for the taxi people and the butcher shop people, they never call twice?"

"So?"

"So," she went on with irreproachable logic, "that means that the taxi stand and butcher shop numbers are probably similar to ours, while the rest of the calls are crossed lines. Or mental patients. Or people who watch *Fox News* all day."

She was, I realized, absolutely correct. Again. Our phone number contains a ridiculous amount of nines, and I could see how it might confuse someone dialing a similar number. Nonetheless…

That night I was awakened once again in the small hours by the relentless ringing of the phone. "Taxi service," I said professionally.

"Oh no," Lucy moaned.

"Yes, I need a taxi," the voice of an American man informed me.

"Where are you calling from?" I asked cheerfully.

The man gave me the name of a gay hotel.

"Okay," I said. Suddenly it dawned upon me that all of the callers wanting taxis had been men. "Will you be standing outside?" I inquired sweetly.

"Can't you just honk?" he asked.

"Oh, heavens no, not at this hour. You just plant your sweet self outside and I'll be there in ten minutes."

"All right," he said reluctantly.

"By the way," I said, dropping my voice to a throaty whisper, "what do you look like?"

"Why do you have to know that?" he demanded testily. "I'll be standing right outside the entrance."

"Well, I don't *have* to know," I said. "But I *do* like your voice and I *am* curious."

"What do *you* look like?" he asked.

"Me? Well, my friends call me 'Hunky', if that gives you an idea."

"*Hunky*?" he and my wife exclaimed in unison.

"That's right," I told them. "My favorite sports are badminton and brunch. I love to take long romantic walks along windswept beaches with a quart of mint chocolate chip ice-cream. I'm partial to rubber, *Cool Whip* and cannelloni. On weekends, I get really wild. Last week, for example…"

Unfortunately, we will never know what I was about to say vis-à-vis my more unorthodox weekend activities, because it was at this point that my wife wrenched the phone from my hand, replacing it vigorously in its receptacle.

"You shouldn't have done that," I complained.

"Please, go to sleep!" Lucy beseeched me.

"All right, honey," I sighed, "I guess you'll never understand."

"Understand what?"

"Male bonding. It's not just a matter of testosterone. It also…"

"Go…to…sleep!" she urged me anew.

When a few seconds later the phone rang again, I picked it up on the first ring.

"*Felatio Cab Company,*" I chirped cheerfully. "We come...you get it!"

Three Colors Short of a Rainbow

Not many men, I would imagine, have been fired (justly or unjustly) by their own wives. In my case the pink-slip was more than justified. In fact, had I been in a position to do so, I would have fired me myself.

The entire sad episode began innocuously enough when, after repeatedly complaining to my Australian ping-pong partner that I could not understand his goofy Outback lingo, he procured for me a small booklet entitled, *Down Under Slang*.

"Here yuh go, mate," he told me, "now yuh can bloody well *gobber* like a bloody *baked bean* for a change."

"What?"

"Read the bloody book."

And read it I did, over and over again, until I'd grown so enamored with the bloody nonsense that I decided to insert an Australian character into my bloody novel.

But merely reading the little book, I soon discovered, was not enough to give me a true working feel for all those wonderful *Down Underisms*. In order to be properly absorbed they needed to be spoken aloud, preferably in the presence of other people. Unfortunately, the only contact I was permitted (by Presidential Decree) with other human beings was in my wife's handicraft shop.

I was sitting in that very location when one of our best clients, a nice but stuffy woman named Mrs. Sutton, walked in and said, "I hope everything is going well for you and your lovely wife."

"*Bob's your uncle!*" (Everything's fine!) I replied cheerily.

"Did you say, 'Bob is my uncle?'" Mrs. Sutton asked disbelievingly.

"*Bingeroo!*" (Right you are!)

"Oh, I see," she said, backing fearfully out the door.

My next clients were a couple from Alaska. After eying several of our exquisite Talavera plates, they asked if there was a discount for purchasing in quantity. In my most polite manner I explained to them that our prices were already so reasonable that discounts were out of the question:

"*On a roo's rear-end!*" I said emphatically.

"I beg your pardon?"

"*Dinky doe-doe,*" (No.) I said, by way of clarification.

"Excuse me," her husband said, angrily approaching the desk, "do you speak English?"

"Of course I do. What do I look like, a *ning-nong*?" I demanded indignantly.

"A what?"

"I'm no *bloody Wally*," I insisted. "Maybe you're the one who's *a railing short of a balcony.*"

As the confused couple left the shop, the telephone rang. It was my wife.

"Have you been hitting the *raicilla*?" she asked without preamble.

"No, honey, I'm *as sober as a deacon's dog.* Why do you ask?"

After a short pause she said, "I just got a phone call from Mrs. Sutton. She said you were acting abnormally."

"Well…abnormal…that's a relative term, honey."

"Mrs. Sutton said you were speaking incoherently."

"Were those her exact words?" I asked.

"Yes."

"Well then, you can tell Mrs. Sutton for me that she has a wonderful way with the English language."

Another moment of silence. "So you're okay?" Lucy asked uncertainly.

"Never been better," I replied. "Gotta go."

Three women from California walked in and began at once to eye with avid interest a row of silver bracelets lined up inside a glass case. "May I?" one of them asked, meaning, could she open the case and inspect the superb pieces at close-hand.

"*Ricky-ticky-tangeroo!*" I said graciously.

"Oh my," one of her companions exclaimed.

"Are these sterling silver?" the third woman asked. "The prices seem awfully low."

"We have *bonzer* prices," I said proudly. "And as for the silver, it's strictly the *bee's knees.*"

"Is the owner around?" the first woman asked anxiously.

"No."

"Do you know where I could locate her?"

"That's hard to say. My wife is quite the ephemeral type. Just like the *Scarlet Pumpernickel*: 'They seek her here, they seek her there, those Aussies seek her…'"

"*You* are Lucy's *husband*?" she asked with astonishment.

"*Does a tick have teeth*?" I replied gaily.

"Poor woman."

An hour later the phone rang once again. "I told you never to call me here," I told my wife.

"What in the world is going on?" Lucy demanded. "I just got another call, from Betty Baker, this time."

"Betty Crocker?"

"Betty Baker. She said she was just in the shop with two of her friends, and that you wouldn't let them buy a bracelet."

"Well, that's a lie," I replied. "I was *as cooperative as a hooker on holiday.*"

As the line went dead a throng of avid shoppers, having just disembarked en masse from the Mismaloya bus, entered the store in similar fashion. None of them wanted to buy anything, naturally, and just as the last of them was leaving my wife burst in, accompanied by our attorney and a licensed psychotherapist.

"What have you been doing?" she demanded breathlessly. "We're losing clients faster than…faster than…"

"*Faster than a dingo's dinner*?" I offered helpfully.

"I don't believe it," she moaned. "You've been practicing your Australian slang in the shop, haven't you?"

"Well…I…He's a very important character," I pointed out.

"Who's an important character? What are you talking about?"

"Bloody Bob, the Aussie photographer. He has a twin brother who's a serial killer, but you don't find that out till the last chapter."

"Okay, I give up," Lucy said, "you're finally fired."

"Permanently?" I asked with bated breath.

Conveniently located right across the street was my favorite bar and there I marched forlornly to drown my sorrows in *Modelo Dark* on tap. Michael, the German owner, after serving me my beer, said in his accented but excellent English, "What's the matter? You look down in the *dumpskenstrudel*."

"Michael," I replied with emotion, "if I've got *a face like a yard of tripe*, and I feel *like a lily on a dustbin*, it's because my wife just *gave me the nozzle*. But she was *Outback Jack*: I had to be stopped: The shop was *going down the gurgler*."

Michael favored me with a brief but compassionate glance. "It's the sun," he told a nearby waiter, "it gets to all these loco gringos sooner than later."

Vallarta 2050

Arnold Plummer was born and raised in Puerto Vallarta, Mexico. When he was twenty-two-years-old, he moved with his family to California where he had a long and successful career as a landscape architect. Forty-five years later, inspired by his fond early memories, he returned to Vallarta with the idea of retiring there.

Puerto Vallarta in the year 2050, Arnold discovered, was a little different from the Vallarta of 2004 which he remembered. First of all, he was pleased to note, the problem of traffic congestion had been all but resolved by a series of creative and ingenious innovations.

Strolling down the malecon, which only allowed vehicular participation between the hours of two and four am every other Monday, Arnold was impressed by the majestic eight-level skyway rising high into the air as it handled all of Vallarta's cross-town vehicular traffic with ease. On the other hand, the "Built For You By United Communications" signs dangling from the skyway at one-meter intervals, Arnold thought he could probably do without.

"Hey Mister!" a metallic voice suddenly called out. "Where are you from?"

Stopping in his tracks Arnold was confronted by his first robot *OPC*, a four-foot-high machine with an open can of motor oil in one mechanical hand, and fifty one-hundred-dollar bills in the other.

Arnold Plummer smiled at the odd-looking automaton and kept on walking.

"No, wait!" the robot cried out. "Don't you want to make five thousand dollars? All you have to do is spend nine minutes of your time…"

"I'm retired," Arnold told the robot. "I'm not interested in making money at all."

"Then how about two hundred cases of pseudo-tequila?" the robot asked. "For just nine minutes…"

"I don't drink," Arnold said, continuing on. "Have a nice day."

"Wait," the robot said, producing a third mechanical arm from an aperture in his derriere. "Shake my pincer."

Arnold regarded the gray metal pincer with distaste. "No thanks," he said.

"Hey, what's the matter," the offended machine demanded, "don't you like Mexican robots?"

Attempting to walk down the malecon proved to be something of a chore. There were, apparently, robot *OPCs* stationed almost everywhere. Some of them rolled out of hidden doors built into the facades of buildings. Some popped up out of manhole covers. Some even floated down from the roofs of buildings on anti-gravity disks. Arnold decided to flag down a solar-powered hovercraft and head over to the more mellow *Romantic Zone*.

But the *Romantic Zone* had changed as well. Somehow it had become *really* romantic. Everywhere Arnold looked, as he strolled down *Olas Altas*, he saw couples kissing, holding hands, giving each other bouquets of flowers, sipping glasses of champagne and wishing each other a "Happy Valentine's Day!" even though it was only November.

Gosh, Arnold thought, I wonder if they still allow women here.

Stopping at one of the twelve hundred sidewalk cafes for a coffee, Arnold was astounded by the amazing variety of beverages and the unexpectedly high prices. A double almond-vanilla-mocha-*raicilla*-espresso, for example, was just under three hundred dollars—and that didn't include the tip! While Arnold sat sipping his sixty-dollar plain decaf, forty-four different entities stopped at his table to offer him various types of services. He politely refused all but the last, a nine-armed robot who offered him a free continuous massage for the next ten years, if he would only give up nine minutes of his time.

Arnold Plummer told him to get lost.

"What's the matter," the mechanical pest demanded, "you got something against nine-armed Mexican masseurs?"

Back at his hotel, after an excellent lunch at one of Vallarta's forty-two thousand world-class restaurants, Arnold tuned the TV to the local *Vallarta Tourist Channel* to find out what kind of activities were available in the evening. He had always enjoyed the bi-weekly Art Walks and hoped that they were still going on.

He need not have worried. There were, according to the TV, Art Walks every night. In fact, Puerto Vallarta's sixteen hundred galleries were holding Art Walks every fifteen minutes, twenty-four hours a day, seven days a week. According to the proud interactive announcer, "Puerto Vallarta is now ranked Number One in the world for most cheap wine consumed on an hourly basis."

"Gee, that's terrific," Arnold told the interactive announcer, "but what about boat tours; what are my options if I want to take a boat tour?"

"Boy, are you in luck!" the interactive TV announcer exclaimed. "We have over a hundred booze cruises alone! We have cruises to Yelapa, Las Animas, Quimixto, Los Arcos, Sayulita, Boca de Tomatlan, San Diego, Anchorage, Boston, Cancun, Omaha…"

"Omaha, Nebraska?" Arnold asked with disbelief.

"No, Omaha Beach in France; you know, where they landed on D-Day in World War II. We also go to…"

"But I don't drink," Arnold said. "Don't you have a boozeless cruise?"

"A cruise with no booze? What are you, crazy?" the interactive TV announcer asked rudely.

"Say, there's no need to take that tone with me, young… uh, whatever," Arnold advised the announcer.

"Oh yeah," the announcer said, "what are you going to do about it?"

"Change the station, for one thing," Arnold replied.

"No wait, I'm sorry," the announcer said. "Please forgive me; it won't happen again."

"All right," Arnold said, "so tell me about some land tours. You must have some land tours that don't include an open bar."

"We sure do," the announcer said with enthusiasm. "We have over fourteen thousand alcohol-free land-based tours. Should I list them in alphabetical order for you?"

"No, no, no," Arnold said, "I'm only here for a month. How about just a list of nature tours?"

"You got it. Okay, there's the *Visit the Place Where They Used to Have Actual Dolphins Tour*; the *Visit a Beach Where They Used to Rescue Actual Turtles Tour*; the *Visit a Tree Tour*; the *Visit a Poisonous Snake Farm Tour*…"

"Poisonous snakes?" Arnold interrupted. "Aren't they dangerous?"

"Well, no. Actually, they're *simulated* snakes. But they look completely real, and you can take one home as a souvenir absolutely free, if you're just willing to give us nine minutes of your time."